Chances

Chances

The probability factors of life

James Burke

VIRGIN

First published in Great Britain in 1991 by
Virgin Books
338 Ladbroke Grove
London W10 5AH

British Library Cataloguing in Publication Data
Burke, James *1936–*
   Chances: risk & odds in everyday life.
   1. Risks
   I. Title
   302

   ISBN 1–85227–393–3

Typeset by Phoenix Photosetting, Chatham, Kent
Printed and bound in Great Britain by
Mackays of Chatham PLC, Chatham, Kent

To Madeline

CONTENTS

I should like to thank Helen O'Leary for
her meticulous research assistance.

INTRODUCTION

What are the chances?

If you can make one heap of all your winnings,
And risk it on one turn of pitch-and-toss,
And lose, and start again at your beginnings,
And never breathe a word about your loss,
Yours is the Earth and everything that's in it. . .

Rudyard Kipling, 'If'

Life is a gamble. Whoever you are, whatever you're doing, the chances are that as you read these words you're involved in a decision about the future. You may be considering a change in your career, hairstyle, weight, house, spouse, name, doctor, money, car, behaviour, clothes. . . or a thousand other things. Whatever the circumstances, the decision you make about what action you should take in the matter will be based on your assessment of its likelihood of success. Most people regard the result of such a decision as a matter of luck. Some even let the choice of action rest on the flip of a coin.

But the future is not a closed book. Between your choice of action and its outcome, various factors will influence your chances of success. This factor may, in the case of the decisions above, take the form of your hairdresser, or a restaurant, estate agent, lover, mother, state of health, bank manager, garage mechanic, boss, shop assistant. The more accurately you can assess *how* these influences will affect the outcome of your decision, the more likely it is that the action you choose to take will result in what you want. Forecasting the future is a matter of knowing about the influences that determine the outcome. A matter of knowing what are the chances.

I

SOME OUTSIDE CHANCES

◆

Do you dream of winning the pools? Are you terrified of thunderstorms? If so, you are certainly not alone. But the odds against being affected by either of these events are impossibly long. So long that perhaps they are not worth considering. After all, the fatalist would say, it's just a matter of luck. Or is it?

It is most unlikely that you will be struck by lightning. But not impossible. Defying the odds by standing in the middle of a field in a thunderstorm will not improve your chances. If we didn't worry about danger just a little bit, we might be more likely to meet it (instead of being somewhere safe when the lightning strikes).

And if someone has to win the pools, there is a chance it

could be you (always assuming you send in the coupon, of course). It's a long shot, but one that's worth the risk if you don't stake too much on it.

Some of our greatest hopes and fears are very unlikely to come true. But whether you hope for the best, fear for the worst, or prefer to take things as they come, the choices you make will be affected by your attitude to fate and chance. After all, nothing ventured nothing gained – but nothing lost either.

The secret of taking risks successfully lies in knowing the odds against you. And then deciding whether, for you, they are worth taking. As you read on, you may be pleasantly surprised to find that everything is not always as you might expect.

What are my chances of being struck by lightning in my lifetime?

1 in 600,000.

What are my chances of winning the football pools with a single ticket?

Not good. The odds against winning an 8-draw pool from ten selections filled in solely by chance are (don't hold your breath) 42,595,495 to 1! You can better these odds a little by employing what are described as 'betting strategies' (better known only to you, of course).

2

SOME GOOD BETS

◆

Many people have a fear of flying. If you are one of them, reassurance is at hand. Flying is far less dangerous than many of the everyday risks we take without a second thought.

There are many understandable reasons for being frightened of flying. For a start, planes have no visible means of support (although birds have been relying on the laws of aerodynamics quite safely for a few million years). You might worry about engine failure or the threat of a terrorist bomb, but in fact planes are maintained to standards far more rigorous than the family car, and security precautions are getting tighter all the time.

The figures speak for themselves. Flying is a surprisingly

good bet – and one well worth taking for the enjoyment that lies in store at the end of the journey.

Compared with other dangers, how risky is air travel?

Not very risky at all. Any time you simply fall down, for example, you are six times more likely to be killed than when you travel by air.

How likely am I still to be alive in another year?

It depends where you live. If you are an average American you can count on it with a high level of confidence. The average American is 99.8 per cent likely to live at least one more year. The average European has an 89.7 per cent chance. You do best in Spain (a 92.3 per cent chance) and worst in the UK (an 88.6 per cent chance). And everywhere, you live longer anyway if you're a woman.

Given the prevalence of terrorism around the world, just how risky is overseas travel?

Overseas travel is very safe. Your chances of being killed by terrorists overseas is 1 in 650,000. You should worry more about being struck by lightning or by being killed by Americans in Baltimore. (The chances of the latter happening are greater than 1 in 4,000). In spite of what you hear about the Sicilian Mafia, Belgium is the riskiest place in Europe (although at 1 in 46,511 it's a long way behind Baltimore).

3

REMEMBER TO WEAR CLEAN UNDERCLOTHES

You Never Know When You'll be in an Accident

Accidents are always waiting to happen. It's in their very nature. But some accidents are more likely than others.

It will come as no surprise that drinking and driving is seriously bad for your health. This may also explain why most road accidents happen late at night. But, contrary to popular myth, men are far more dangerous on the road than women. And who would have thought that Sunday is the safest day to drive? Hiding at home may avoid the carnage on the roads, but even there life is not without its dangers — though often in unexpected forms.

If you tried to avoid all the accident black spots at home and in the car you would be in and out of the house like the dolls in a weatherhouse or a demented cuckoo in a broken clock. You might, for example, make a point of staying at home after 10 p.m., all day on Friday and during the whole of July, while also making sure that you are away from the house between midday and 8 p.m. and throughout April. This regime might be difficult to maintain and would certainly increase your chances of being unemployed. Becoming self-employed could be one solution, but whatever you do don't become a builder or a farmer. People in these occupations are very accident-prone.

As an alternative, you could resort to simple common sense. After all, accidents are, by definition, unforeseen or unexpected events. You simply cannot avoid all of the risks all of the time. But take care anyway!

If I drive a lot, on which day of the week is it most important that I wear clean underclothes?

If you are determined not to humiliate your mother or yourself, make sure your underclothes are particularly fresh on Friday – far and away the most dangerous day of the week on which to drive. You can be considerably more careless about your hygiene on Sunday. In spite of what they say about weekend drivers, it's 25 per cent less dangerous than any other day. You are most likely to be killed in a road accident between the hours of 10 p.m. and 4 a.m. That's when 15.5 per cent of all accidents happen.

How much safer are large commercial airlines than smaller commuter lines?

The major airlines are 500 times safer.

My plane has just taken off – what are the chances that it will crash and someone will be killed?

Small. There is a 1.6 in 10,000,000 chance your flight will crash and someone will be killed. Every time you draw breath, somewhere in the world an airliner takes off or lands in safety. Enjoy yourself.

Which toy is the riskiest?

The two-wheeled peril, the bicycle. In the US, it accounts for an astounding 385,000 emergency hospital visits among children under fifteen. Falling off a bike accounts for almost all of this trauma. In Europe, playground swings cause half as many accidents.

In terms of fatal accidents, which month is safest and which is the riskiest?

Save the money you'd spend on swimming suits and surfboards for ice skates and scarves. July – by an enormous margin – is the most fatal month for accidents, February the most benign. Where you live makes a difference. In Europe, road deaths are highest in Portugal (26.4 per 1,000), lowest in the Netherlands (10.5). That compares well with the US (19) and Australia (18). Japan is safest (10). Specifically, if you're riding a motorbike, avoid Ireland.

Should I stay at home and better my chances?

If you do, remember domestic accidents happen most in April (the worst month for any kind of accident involving children between 0–14) and least in November.

In terms of injury, what's the safest sport?

It's safer to be in the air (hang-gliding, aerobatics, gliding) than up the mountain. Birdmen run about the same risks as watersports enthusiasts. Motor sport is the only activity which is as dangerous as mountaineering.

In terms of physical injury, is it riskier to be a farmer or a metropolitan policeman?

Compared with the perils faced by the typical farmer, even inner-city bobbies might as well be on holiday. Farm injuries are among the most prevalent and violent experienced by any occupational group.

How much more likely am I to be involved in a car accident if I drive (or am a passenger) in a small car, than if I drive (or am a passenger) in a large car?

Not at all more likely. On the contrary, the largest-sized cars are more often involved in fatal accidents than are the small and mini cars.

Is there a difference between men and women when it comes to accidents while at the wheel?

Very much so. On average, 1 male driver in 300 will be killed at the wheel. For women drivers the figure is 1 in 850. 47 per cent of male drivers will be involved in some kind of accident while driving, compared with only 29 per cent of women drivers. So let your wife or girlfriend be the chauffeur!

Will cross-training in several sports at once decrease my risk of exercise-related injury?

No. It will increase it substantially. Triathletes who compete in running, swimming, and cycling have been shown, in some surveys, to suffer up to nearly 3 times as many injuries as those who train for and compete only in swimming. Those who compete only in running or cycling also have far fewer injuries.

Am I more likely to die from an accident related to firearms or one related to electric current?

The firearms are about twice as likely to kill you accidentally. However, firearm incidents are extremely rare. You are more likely to die from accidental drowning than from a firearm. As for death by shock, you're more likely to die from choking on food.

What are the best times to stay out of the house so as to avoid a domestic accident?

Don't be there between noon and 8 p.m. That's when 40 per cent of accidents occur. Contrary to popular belief, late night and early morning are safe times. Only 5.8 and 1.7 per cent of accidents happen then.

What are the chances that I will be injured in a road accident this year?

About 1 in 10,000. That's 37 times less likely than the chances of dying from heart disease.

In those countries that have seat-belt laws, has the risk of injury or death in road accidents been substantially reduced?

Yes. The laws have resulted in nearly 7 per cent fewer deaths and 10 per cent fewer serious injuries. However, while European road deaths have been falling in general (20 per cent since the mid 70s), in Spain and Greece during the same period, deaths have increased by 21 and 37 per cent.

In those countries with higher speed limits has there been any appreciable increase in road fatalities?

The best study to date indicates a negligible increase of 1 per cent. Researchers in West Germany, incidentally, have declared the country's 5,000-mile autobahn system (which has no speed limit) 'the safest road' in Germany. It accounts for only 4 per cent of the nation's road accidents – and most of those occur in construction zones where there are temporary speed limits.

What time am I most likely to be breathalysed?

Most blowing goes on between 10 p.m. and midnight. For some reason, between midnight and 1 a.m. you're only half as likely to be tested. But watch out after lunch. The third most frequent testing hour is 4 p.m.! And just in case you're thinking of using these statistics to drink and drive – don't. Nearly 1 in 5 road deaths are alcohol-related.
P.S. You only die once.

Who are least likely to wear seat belts, men or women?

Men. Also among the least likely to use seat belts are people under the age of thirty and drunken drivers.

What is the risk that a teenager will not use a seat belt?

56 per cent.

How effective are seat belts in preventing fatal injuries?

40 per cent to 50 per cent when properly used.

In terms of fatalities, is it riskier to drive in Japan or the US?

Japan is about 75 per cent riskier.

In general, what's the riskiest European country to drive in?

For casualties per head of population, Belgium is the worst (34 times riskier than driving in Ireland). For fatalities, avoid France (more than twice as dangerous as the UK).

In terms of fatal accidents, are motorcycles really much more risky than cars?

Motorcycles are nearly 14 times more likely to kill you. In Europe, keep your machine off Irish roads, where there are by far the most motorcycle deaths (2,000 for every 1,000,000 vehicles).

Are rural dwellers, suburbanites or city dwellers the most likely to be killed in non-motor vehicle accidents?

Country types are almost twice as likely as suburbanites to be felled in this way. City dwellers fall in the middle range. And the range is quite broad: the risks in the country are 34 per cent above the national average and 31 per cent below those in the suburbs.

I am planning a long trip across Europe. What's the safest way of getting to my destination – car, plane, or train?

Go by train. Your chances of being killed on the train are only 0.15 in a million, about half what they'd be on a plane. Your chances of being killed if you drive to your destination are 31 times greater than if you go by train.

Which place offers the best chance of almost totally avoiding a fatal accident?

Luxembourg. There are 164 times fewer fatal accidents there than in France (where you're most likely to have one).

Is my child at greater risk of being killed or disabled by accident, by drugs, or by childhood disease?

Accidents account for more death and disability among children than drugs and all childhood diseases combined.

How dangerous is the sort of diving accident where the victim plunges into too-shallow water head first?

Very dangerous. This type of accident leaves half of all its victims paralysed from the neck down.

What are the chances that, as a beginner, I will be injured on the ski slopes?

Not too high – 1 in 300.

In which line of work am I most likely to have an occupational injury?

Energy- or water-supply and construction. These have the highest employee injury rates of all. If you're self-employed and in construction, you account for no less than 69.5 per cent of all work-related injuries! You're 30 times safer being a banker (the safest of all jobs in terms of occupational injury).

Which part of my body is at greatest risk in a work-related accident? My fingers, legs, or torso?

Torso – injured in 32 per cent of all accidents. Fingers and legs are injured in only 14 per cent and 13 per cent of all accidents, respectively.

Among household cleaning items and appliances, does a washing machine or a hot iron pose the greater danger?

From the safety point of view, stick to ironing. The washing machine causes more injuries than any other laundry item in home use. Bleach comes in second, the iron third.

In terms of accidental injuries, how risky is the bathroom?

Pretty safe. Most accidents in the bathroom happen because of a fall. But they're only 2.3 per cent of all domestic accidents. The real danger zones are the living/dining room (12.2 per cent – falls predominate again), then the kitchen (11.8 per cent).

Am I more likely to burn something or break something this year?

You're 4.4 times more likely to visit the Accident and Emergency Unit for fractures than for a domestic burn.

What are the chances I'll be injured or killed in a residential fire this year?

Low. Only 0.02 per cent of accidental deaths are due to this cause.

What are the chances I'll be injured or killed in a B&B/hotel fire this year?

Very low. Of the total number of fires in 'occupied dwellings' last year, only 1.7 per cent happened in hotels, B&Bs, motels or hostels. You're safer away from home!

Which dogs are most likely to bite?

Alsatians, followed by (in this order) Chows, Airedales, and Pekingese.

Which dogs are most likely/least likely to assume friendly attitudes towards children?

There are many exceptions, of course, but the experts say that boxers, Newfoundlands, bloodhounds, Bernese mountain dogs, Samoyeds, Labrador retrievers, beagles, Boston terriers, Cocker spaniels, and pugs are most likely to get along with kids. Least inclined to tolerate children are (surprising in view of their soft looks), the St Bernard and the old English sheepdog, along with the Alaskan malamute, the bull terrier, and (proving that small doesn't always take to small) the toy poodle.

4

MARRIAGE, DIVORCE, SEX

And other romantic dangers

Marriage is a minefield into which the unwary male ventures at his peril, while a romantic white wedding is a woman's only goal and the beginning of happiness ever after. These are the myths of the pub and the romantic novel. The statistics tell a different story.

Given the opportunity, most men seem prepared to take the risk of entering the danger zone. A lot of people marry. More than two-thirds of them stay married. And a very high percentage of those whose marriages fail take the plunge again in the proverbial triumph of hope over experience. Interestingly, once men have tried marriage they are far keener than once-bitten women to have another go. The figures lend some support to their eagerness. On several counts marriage is good for your health, though what it does for your happiness is not quite so clear.

So how can you increase your chances of getting married and staying that way? It helps to be in the right country at the right time. The ratio of men to women at different ages varies so much that you will have to identify your place on the age scale and move accordingly. After that you are on your own. If you do meet your Mr or Miss Right and you want to stay together for ever, marry early or late, but don't follow the herd and marry in your twenties – and don't live together first.

Being well-educated helps to prevent divorce, but too much education reduces the chances of marrying at all if you are a woman. Spare a thought for the graduate spinster of forty, whose prospects of marriage are dismal indeed. But save your pity. More and more people are happily unmarried, and women whose marriages have failed seem to relish their single state far more than men. So much for the myths.

Where am I most likely to marry?

The highest European marriage rates are in the UK and Portugal (7 in every 1,000). If you're intent on tying the knot at all costs, avoid France and Spain (4.7 in every 1,000).

What are my chances of marrying if I am 16 years old or older?

It depends where you live. Your chances of marrying between age 15 and 19 are 13.8 per cent in Greece, 8.9 in Portugal, 8.8 in the USA. Your chances are least in Denmark (0.7) and France (0.8). The UK comes midway (4.5).

If I want to marry a very young woman/man, where are my chances the greatest?

In descending order of opportunity: Spain (where the legal age is only 12!), Portugal (14), Luxembourg (15).

Is the risk of remaining unmarried greater for men or women?

Men stalwartly shoulder the greater risk here, at least during their younger years. Men are 37 per cent more likely to remain single – but only up until the age of 55. At that point the situation shifts a bit, when women over the age of 55 are 5 per cent more likely never to have married.

What are the chances I will marry someone of another nationality?

Less than 1 in 50.

What are the current chances that my spouse and I will have three or more children?

Under 11 per cent. In 1960, the chances would have been greater than 20 per cent.

If I am a professional woman, how likely am I to find romance on the job?

Very likely – about 55 per cent. And the office romance is likely to last longer than those that originate in bars or health clubs.

How likely is it that, if we don't divorce, both my spouse and I will live to celebrate our fortieth anniversary?

Pretty good. In fact, two out of three marriages that avoid divorce will last more than forty years. This is a considerable improvement over the situation in 1900, when only one in three marriages lasted to forty years without the death of one partner.

What are the chances I will still be a virgin when I am 16?

29 per cent.

How risky is it for a woman to ask a man to go out with her?

Not very. In fact, 71 per cent of all unattached men say they would welcome a woman taking the initiative.

Are the overall chances that I will marry going up or down with time?

Up. But hurry. Throughout Europe the average age of marriage has been steadily rising. But it's still now only at 24.2 (women) and 26.4 (men). However, the overall rate of marriage is dropping from 6.8 in 1,000 (1977) to 5.7 in 1,000 (1990).

Am I likely to find happiness in marriage?

Married people, according to a recent survey, still count them-selves happier than unmarried people – but the happiness gap between the two groups is narrowing significantly. It seems that more and more people are finding themselves just as happy to stay unmarried. A dozen years ago there were 20 per cent more married men (between the ages of 25 and 39) than unmarried men who described themselves as 'very happy'. Today there are only 5.7 per cent more 'very happy' married men. Among women, the difference has slipped from nearly 30 per cent a dozen years ago to only 12 per cent today.

In what month am I most/least likely to get married?

If you are afraid of marriage, lock yourself up on your own in the month of June. Emerge in January – the month of fewest marriages.

If I am a university-educated woman and I have not married by the time I reach age 40, how likely is it that I will ever marry?

Less than 1 per cent. If a woman has not married by the time she is 35, there is only a 5 per cent chance she will marry.

I have my eye on a 45-year-old man who has never married. What are the chances I can lead him to the altar?

Throw some mothballs on your wedding dress. Your chances of bagging this one are only 1.2 per cent.

At what age are most people likely to marry?

It depends where you live. In the UK the average age at first marriage is 26.2 (men) and 24.1 (women). In Denmark the ages are 29.2 (men) and 26.5 (women).

As a girl who wants a fellow, at which age am I most likely to hook one, based on their overall availability?

Alas, you'd practically have to rob the cradle. Under the age of 14, boys outnumber girls, but only by 5 per cent. After 14 girls' numbers gradually increase until at 50 they are equal. After that there are more women than men. Your best bet is to get your man as early as possible.

I'd like to marry a younger man. What are my chances?

About 33 per cent overall – considerably better than they were ten years ago.

If I'm 21 and not married, should I be worried?

No. The median age of both males and females at first marriage is steadily moving higher.

What are the chances that a woman, divorced or widowed between the ages of 15 and 44, will remarry within one year or three years?

30 per cent remarry within one year, 47 per cent within three years. The men move faster: 42 per cent within the year and 60 per cent within three.

What are the chances, overall, that I'll remarry after divorce?

78 per cent for women, 83 per cent for men.

What are the chances my marriage will end in divorce?

28 per cent.

If a fellow marries at the age of 16, how much more likely is it that he will get divorced than a man who marries at the age of 24?

Not at all more likely. The just-past-puberty groom is more likely to stay married than the world- and woman-weary 24-year-old.

Do my chances of remaining married go up or down with time?

Up. The first four years are the riskiest, with divorce rates of 28.4 per cent. After that the rate falls. After 30 years you've only got a 4.3 per cent chance of breaking apart.

I'm a teenager whose parents have just divorced. Will this unpleasant experience make me more or less likely to divorce someday?

The offspring of parents who divorce are themselves more likely to divorce than are the children of those who remain married. For females this greater likelihood amounts to 50 per cent, for males, 23 per cent.

Having risked and carried through with divorce, are men or women more satisfied with their newly regained single status?

It's the divorced or separated woman who does most of the sighing. . . but these are sighs of relief! Some 85 per cent of divorced or separated women say they are happy with their single status. Only 58 per cent of the men are as content.

What are the chances my marriage will last forever?

Slim, especially if you live in the UK, where last year compared with 398,000 marriages there were no less than 165,000 divorces. The average duration of marriage in the UK is between 5 and 9 years.

Where in Europe are couples most/least likely to divorce?

Most likely in the UK (12.9 per thousand marriages) and Denmark (12.8). Least likely in Greece (3). Least of all in Ireland (divorce is illegal!).

Are better- or lesser-educated women more likely to divorce?

Education and divorce are inversely related, meaning the more you have of one, the less you have of the other. The less-educated populace divorce not only more often but also earlier.

Are better-educated or lesser-educated women, divorced or widowed between the ages of 15 and 44, more likely to remarry?

The less education a woman has, the more likely she is to remarry.

Will 'cohabiting' – living together without being married – improve our chances for a lasting marriage if we finally do tie the knot?

That's the common wisdom in many circles, but a recent study of Swedish couples indicates this is not the case. In fact, among those who live together in Sweden before marriage there is an 80 per cent greater chance of divorce. Swedish social trends tend to precede those in other countries by a decade.

Is a person who marries at the age of 24 more likely to end up getting divorced than a person who marries at the age of 34?

Yes, considerably more likely, and this is true for both men and women. The divorce rate is particularly high for people who marry in their twenties. The rate steadily declines with age thereafter.

As a divorced woman, what are the chances I'll get alimony?

About 6 per cent of all divorced women get alimony, although on average 33 per cent have to go to court to enforce regular payment! Among divorced women who remarry, less than 1 per cent are still paid alimony by their former husbands. 1 per cent of husbands owing alimony go to jail for non-payment.

I'm an about-to-be-divorced father. What are my chances my child will live with me rather than with the mother?

In two cases out of three the courts tend to find in favour of the mother.

Are those who have 'loved and lost' more likely to die than those who have never married?

The divorced/separated are at lower risk of dying next year than those who have never married.

Do marriage and divorce have any influence on heart attack risks?

Yes. Marriage seems to reduce the risk for males. Married men have a 6 per cent lower chance of dying from a heart attack than do separated/divorced males and a 23 per cent lower risk than men who have never married. For women, marriage also protects against heart attacks – unless the marriage leads to divorce or separation, in which case the risk of heart attack soars: to 37 per cent more than the risk experienced by women still married; to 33 per cent more than the risk for those women who never marry.

Is marriage good for immunity?

Yes, according to an Ohio State University study the immune systems of married women were found to be functioning better than those of unmarried women. Happy marriages produced even healthier immune systems.

Does going beyond a first degree into postgraduate work have any effect on a woman's marriage prospects?

Yes, it diminishes them considerably. Women with postgraduate education are three times less likely to marry than are women with no more than secondary school education.

What are the chances I'll be giving somebody a Valentine's Day card?

High, especially if you're a woman. They buy 56 per cent of all Valentine cards sold. And this is the time of year when men are on their biggest annual card-buying spree!

What are the chances that my son will spend more on a gift or flowers for his sweetheart on Valentine's Day than he will on something for me on Mother's Day?

Sky-high. Retailers say men are more stingy when it comes to Mother's Day gifts and reckless by comparison when it comes to Valentine's Day gifts and flowers.

In view of the AIDS risk, I'm interested in knowing if single women between the ages of 18 and 44 are more or less sexually active than they used to be.

More active, if their responses to a recent survey are to be believed. Over the last five years the numbers of those who are against pre-marital sex have dropped from 28 to 25 per cent.

Are women who read a lot of romance novels more likely to be lousy lovers?

On the contrary. The common wisdom is that such women 'sublimate' sexual urges by reading these novels, but a recent survey indicates that the romance novel addict has sex 74 per cent more often than those who read more staid – and apparently less stimulating – material.

Which sexually transmitted disease am I most likely to contract?

That depends upon your individual sexual preferences and activities, but overall chlamydia (non-specific genital infection) is, far and away, the more frequently transmitted sexual disease. It is three times as frequent as gonorrhea, eight times as frequent as herpes and fifty times as frequent as syphilis.

Does having sex the night before an athletic event reduce one's chances of winning that event or of performing well in it?

This myth was recently put to bed by a study at Colorado State University. Pre-event abstainers did no better than indulgers.

Stamina, agility, reaction time, muscle power and all the other variables were virtually the same in both test groups.

How likely is it that, as a woman between the ages of 40 and 44, I'll have sexual intercourse more than twice a week?

35 per cent.

What are the chances the single woman on whom I have my eye at the moment approves of premarital sex?

High, if she's between 15 and 25. 72 per cent of this age group approve, although 35 per cent of them would only indulge with someone they'd known 'for very long'.

What are the chances my marriage will be of the 'shotgun' variety – the result of pregnancy?

About 15 per cent of all marriages are thus initiated. A recent study reveals that such marriages are not as shaky as previously believed. More than a third of them are still intact after ten years.

What are the chances a baby will be born to parents who aren't married?

It depends where you live. In Europe most illegitimate births occur in Denmark (where they are nearly half of all births). The figure drops to 25 per cent in the UK and France. In Greece only 18.2 births in 1,000 are illegitimate.

What are the chances that, as a teenager, I'll never have sex?

Not great. Some 70 per cent of teenage girls and 80 per cent of teenage boys have sex at least once during their teen years. By the age of 16, half of all teenagers have had at least one sexual encounter.

How widespread is the use of contraceptive techniques?

It varies from place to place and with age group. In women under 45 contraceptive techniques are adopted by 81 per cent in the UK, by 59 per cent in Spain. Only 11 per cent of Spanish 17–19-year-olds of both sexes practiced contraception, compared with 66 per cent in France. For single young women, however, West Germans came highest at 95 per cent.

What are the chances my teenage son thinks it's permissible for a husband to rape his wife or for a man to rape his girlfriend?

One survey indicates that 86 per cent of boys aged 13 to 15 thinks it's permissible for a husband to rape his wife; 24 per cent say it's okay for a man to rape his girlfriend if he's spent 'a lot of money' on her. This is less of an academic matter than you might think. 14 per cent of women who have been married consider they have been raped by their partner, 22 per cent that they had been forced into sex against their will at some time.

I'm a teenage girl planning to have sex with a teenage boy. What are the chances he will use a condom?

Least, at 20 per cent, in the UK. Most, at 43 per cent, in Spain.

I'm a teenage boy with the same thoughts in mind.

Go to France, where teenage use of the contraceptive pill stands at 86 per cent. In Spain, only 29 per cent.

What are the chances my teenage lover will have a sexually transmitted disease?

Pretty good, unfortunately. 1 in 7 carries such an infection.

In which European country am I most likely to find an eligible man?

It depends on your age group. Between 15 and 64: West Germany has 178,000 extra men, the Netherlands 133,000, the UK 77,000 and Denmark only 42,000. However your chances are slim in Italy, where women in this age group outnumber men by 328,000! In the 15–29 group, the news is not so good. Here, European women outnumber men by over a million.

Is there risk from a person who has herpes but currently has no active lesions?

Yes. The risk is actually slight – individuals without active lesions are shedding virus only about 0.5 to 1.5 per cent of the time. But since there is no way of telling when shedding is occurring, those with herpes are advised to use condoms whenever they have sex.

What are the chances my bride will be a virgin?

20 per cent or less. If you had married 25 years ago, the chances would have been 50 per cent.

In what nation of the Western world is the risk of unintended pregnancy the greatest?

In the United States. In view of this it is not surprising that the US, among Western nations, also has the highest rate of abortion per capita. Abortion figures for Europe vary. In Italy, Denmark and Sweden one in every four pregnancies ends in legal abortion. In West Germany only one in ten. In Turkey (the lowest), one in twenty.

Is hair on a man's face or his chest a bigger turn-on for women?

Hair on the face is risky. The majority of women say they now prefer their men clean-shaven. On the other hand, they prefer hairy to smooth chests.

As a women with average breast-size, I wonder what are the chances men will find my better-endowed sisters more attractive?

You're in luck. The majority of men now say they actually prefer average-sized breasts to larger ones.

Are men or women at greater risk of becoming full of themselves?

Behold the strutting male, 28 per cent of whom consider themselves handsome. Only 13 per cent of all women think they are pretty.

To what extent is not having blonde hair a drawback in a woman looking for a man?

Not at all, provided you have long brunette hair, which men now say they find as attractive as long blonde hair.

As a man, I'm wondering if it is riskier to have short or long, curly or straight hair when it comes to attracting the opposite sex.

Long straight hair poses the greatest peril at the present time. More women prefer short curly dark hair on a man than any other type of hair.

In view of all the adverse publicity about the negative effects of too much sun, is the once-popular tan coming to be regarded as a fashion don't? Is it losing its sex appeal?

No. The once-popular tan is the still-popular tan. A majority of both men and women still find a tan a turn-on.

If I want better sex, is the purchase of a water bed a good investment?

Difficult to say. Only 33 per cent of those who buy water beds say sex is better on them.

As a working woman, what are the chances I will be sexually harassed by male colleagues/supervisors?

A recent European survey revealed that French women feel most at risk. 8 per cent felt they had been 'victims of sexual blackmail', although in a UK survey 36 per cent of all workers said they had suffered some form of sexual harassment.

I'd like to know, as a woman, what is the risk that I will one day have unwanted intercourse with a man simply because he continually puts pressure on me to go to bed with him.

The answer will, unfortunately, dishearten many women and encourage certain men: 25 per cent.

What is the risk that a woman will have unwanted sexual intercourse at some point in her life because a man has threatened her with physical force or actually used it to coerce her?

9 per cent.

What is the risk that a woman will have unwanted intercourse with a man who uses his higher authority at work to coerce her?

2 per cent. A recent UK survey indicated that 13 per cent of reported cases of sexual harassment at work involved direct propositions of sexual intercourse.

Are men or women at higher risk of encountering longer waits at public conveniences?

Women definitely have to queue for longer. That's because women take longer. In fact, according to a recent study, they take an average of 34 seconds longer than men to use a public convenience. Women average 79 seconds, men 45. On the basis of these findings, one researcher has concluded that the 'toilet ratio' should be altered, from its current status roughly 50–50, to 60–40 in favour of women. The state of Washington, USA is already paying heed, building more toilets for women along its motorways. Meanwhile, next time you're in an airliner (or anywhere the sexes use the same conveniences) and you have to 'go' in a hurry, you'll know which queue to choose. As a rough rule of thumb, just remember that, in this context, it takes 7.5 men to equal 10 women.

5

CRIME AND PUNISHMENT

◆

Crime statistics make grim reading, and they seem to get worse every year. There is a school of thought which says that crime is not actually on the increase, only the reporting of crime. And in fact we live in far less violent times than even our recent ancestors. But the fear of violence is very real, particularly among the physically vulnerable. Lurid reports in the newspapers and on television tend to confirm all our worst fears, giving the impression that brutal murders and vicious rapes are commonplace events. But these stories get so much coverage because they are in reality quite rare.

The crimes that cause most of us the greatest fear are among the least likely to happen. It is a sad fact that you are more likely to be murdered by your nearest and dearest than by a stranger. And you are even more likely to kill yourself than be killed by someone else.

Even the places with the worst reputations are not necessarily the most dangerous. Crime is actually on the decrease in the US, and the highest UK crime rates are not where you might expect. There are surprises in Europe as well. Luxembourg, Denmark and Belgium all feature prominently in the statistics, and not because their rates of violent crime are low. Italy, despite the reputation of its men, is the safest place for a woman travelling alone.

In fact, women and the elderly are at far less risk of being the victims of crime than men and the young. And crime against the elderly has actually gone down dramatically during the last two decades. These facts should provide some comfort, but it is not surprising if they don't because we are naturally inclined to feel afraid of events against which we can take only limited precautions. Psychopaths are wild cards – but, like wild cards, they turn up rarely.

Happily there are precautions which can be taken against burglary and theft. This is fortunate since these are probably the most common crimes. According to the police, the majority of these crimes are committed by opportunists taking advantage of open windows and doors. So don't take the risk of not locking up. Watch out – there's a thief about!

In what month am I most likely to be shot to death, poisoned, or strangled?

In December.

What are the chances I will be burgled this year if I live in a small town?

A 1 in 25 chance. Resist that offer of a job in the inner city, where the risk is 1 in 10.

What are the chances I will be the victim of a serious crime in my lifetime?

1 in 25. But if you're out of work, the risk is 1.75 per cent more than that.

How much more likely am I to be robbed than murdered?

Hold on to your wallet. 50 times more likely.

If I live in a city of 250,000 or more, how much more likely am I to be murdered than if I live in a town of fewer than 10,000 people?

6.4 times more likely.

What are the chances that the person who murders me is someone I know?

64 per cent.

If I am raped, robbed, or assaulted, what is the likelihood that the assailant is of my own ethnic group?

About 45 per cent overall.

Are men or women more likely to be the victims of violent crime?

Men are 62 per cent of victims. They are also twice as likely as women to commit murder.

Are the rich at higher risk of having their homes burgled?

No. Those with family incomes of less than £12,000 annually are about 30 per cent more likely to be burgled than those with family incomes of £30,000 upwards.

Am I more at risk of burglary in a house which I own or in rented premises?

You're four times more likely to be burgled if you're paying rent.

Am I more likely to be murdered or to kill myself?

It depends where you live, but in general you're more likely to do yourself in, especially in Denmark (European suicide centre) with over 30 times more suicides than murders. The UK figure is 14 to 1.

Am I at higher risk of being the victim of a violent crime in the daytime or at night?

Violence is as likely to befall you in broad daylight as it is under cover of darkness, with one exception: rape. You are 2.7 times more likely to be raped at night.

Does having a lot of people in my household reduce the risk of a burglar succeeding in making off with our goods?

No. In this context, at least, there is no safety in numbers. The risk of successful burglary actually increases the more people there are in your household. The chances of successful burglary in a 6-plus household, for example, are about 65 per cent greater than in a single-person household. So don't start advertising for someone to share your home – at least, not for that reason.

Are you more likely to be murdered over matters related to money or romance?

While it may be true that money can't buy you love, it is more likely to cost you your life. You are 13 per cent more likely to be murdered over an argument concerning money than over disputes related to 'another man' or 'another woman'.

Is arguing risky?

If you value your life, yes. Approximately 50 per cent of all murders occur during arguments.

If I'm robbed, how likely is it I will lose £500 or more?

About 10 per cent of robberies involve sums above this figure.

As I grow older, am I at greater risk of being robbed?

No. From the age of 24 onwards, your chances of being robbed actually diminish steadily. Those who are 65 and over are about 6.5 times less likely to be robbed than those who are 20 to 24. The same general trend occurs in all crime.

Is the risk of being robbed greater for males or females?

Males are twice as likely to be robbed as females.

Am I more likely to be raped on the street or inside a building?

60 per cent of all rapes occur inside buildings; 31 per cent of these occur in the victim's own home or on the victim's property. Only 14 per cent of all rapes occur in the street.

What is the risk I will be sexually assaulted by someone I know?

Only 46 per cent of such acts are committed by strangers. 29 per cent of assailants are acquaintances, 9 per cent are persons 'in a position of trust' and 3 per cent are relatives.

Will taking self-protective measures when someone attempts to rob me increase my chances of being badly hurt?

0.5 per cent of those who resist are killed.

Will taking self-protective measures when someone attempts to rob me reduce the chances of that attempt being successful?

Yes, by 52 per cent.

Does marriage in any way reduce the chances of my being a victim of violent crime?

Yes. Single men and women are more than 3.5 times more likely to be victims of violent crime than are married men. Divorced or separated women are at even greater risk than single women.

Is a car than I hire or own more likely to be stolen?

Apparently you are more careless with cars that don't actually belong to you. The rate of thefts for hire cars is more than double.

How likely is it that if someone tries to snatch my bag they will get away with it?

Prepare to go shopping – for a new bag. The likelihood is 80 per cent.

How likely are the police to catch somebody who robs me?

A little more than 1 in 10 thieves are brought to justice.

Are the risks of being raped different for women who are married/single/divorced/separated?

Yes. Those who are divorced or separated are about 12 per cent more likely to be raped than those who are single and about 7.5 times more likely than those who are married.

Do car alarm systems really reduce the risk of theft?

Yes. Insurance companies report 30 per cent fewer claims for vehicles with these systems.

What are the chances that, as a young male offender, I'll offend again and wind up back in detention within two years?

65 per cent.

Is violent crime in America escalating as fast as we think it is?

It's not escalating at all. Even though non-violent crime in some sectors (such as government) seems to be increasing rapidly, the overall rate of violent crime in America has actually declined slightly in recent years, according to the US Justice Department.

Are things getting worse in Europe?

In general, yes, although it depends where you live. In the last ten years Luxembourg's murder rate has risen three times. Over the same period all other European countries' rates have also risen, with the exception of the Netherlands, where the rate has fallen seven times!

Are the elderly at greater or lesser risk than the young of being crime victims?

The elderly are only half as likely as the young to be crime victims. Moreover, crimes against the elderly have declined 50 per cent in the last fifteen years. Only 8.5 per cent of all crime victims are over 70.

Is it financially riskier for society to release repeat offenders early or to build more prisons?

A US Department of Justice survey has challenged the idea that we can't afford to keep repeat offenders in prison. The study concluded that while it costs society $25,000 per year to keep a prisoner incarcerated, the bill for letting one go early is about $430,000 per year. Almost all re-offenders return to lives of crime, and the $430,000 is calculated on the basis of the average victim losses, police, probation, court, and private security expenses. Looked at another way, the study found that for every 1,000 offenders kept in prison, society saves a net $405 million. We may be looking at a new high-growth industry.

Is a woman more likely to go to prison today than she was a decade ago?

Yes. The chances are growing at a rate of 8 per cent a year.

Am I more likely to meet violence in the big city or in the most isolated parts of the country?

Latest UK rates per head of population of crimes against the person were highest in Nottinghamshire and Humberside, not in the metropolitan areas.

Which ethnic group is most likely to be imprisoned for a drugs offence?

There's a 77 per cent chance you're white, 13.5 per cent chance you're black and only 2 per cent chance you're Chinese.

If I'm convicted of murder, what are the chances I'll get life?

44 per cent.

If I go to court accused of an indictable offence, what are my chances of getting off?

13 per cent of such cases are found not guilty.

What is the risk a police officer will be killed in the line of duty?

Less than 0.5 per cent.

If I'm tried for murder, what are the chances the jury's verdict will be guilty?

High. The conviction rate is 82 per cent.

If I'm found guilty of murder, what are the chances I will actually be imprisoned?

Surprisingly, not 100 per cent, but 82 per cent. The rest are suspended sentences, referrals to youth detention centres, hospital, etc.

If I indulge in forgery or counterfeiting, what is the risk of ending up in court? And if I am found guilty, how likely am I to actually have to spend time in prison?

There's a 67 per cent chance you will be found guilty, and a 62 per cent chance you'll go to prison.

Are those found guilty of burglary or of fraud and forgery more likely to be caught?

The fraudsters. Clear-up rate for fraud and forgery is 67 per cent, while only 27 per cent of burglars are caught.

Apart from the obvious – loss of valuables and possible injury – are there hidden risks in being burgled or robbed?

Yes. A recent US survey showed that nearly 20 per cent of those robbed are so disturbed by the event that they move to a new location shortly afterward.

Are men or women at greater risk of killing themselves with poison?

Women. Poison is the preferred method – in 58 per cent of all female suicides. Oddly enough, when it comes to killing others, poison is only used in 2 per cent of cases.

In which European country is one most likely/least likely to encounter violent crime?

The highest rate is found in Belgium. The lowest (by nearly three times) is the Republic of Ireland.

I'm visiting the US. Where is the real danger spot?

Detroit, where there are 2,375 violent crimes a year per 100,000 population. The safest cities are San Diego and San Antonio, where the violent crime rate is four times lower.

Where in Europe am I most likely to be the victim of robbery with violence?

The likelihood is greatest in Spain – lowest in Greece and Portugal.

Where in the world am I most/least likely to be robbed?

Asia, followed by Latin America and the Caribbean. The Asian robbery rate is thirteen times that of Japan, the country where robbery rates are lowest.

Where is a woman most likely/least likely to be raped?

In Europe, Denmark is the most likely country. There the rate is 11.47 per 100,000. The least likely place is Italy with 1.2 per 100,000. (The US rate is 37.5.)

Where in Europe am I most/least likely to be murdered?

At 7 murders per 100,000 people, the murder rate is highest (would you believe?) in Luxembourg. You're safest in Ireland, where the rate is 0.62.

Where in Europe is the risk of theft greatest/least?

Greatest in Denmark, where the rate is 8,046 per 100,000. Least in Greece, at 354 per 100,000.

And in the US?

The risk is greatest in Washington, D.C., about double that of California, itself a very high-risk state for robberies. The risk is lowest in South Dakota and Montana.

Where in Europe am I at greatest/least risk of having my car stolen?

Keep a vehicular eye out in the UK, where the risk is 823 in 100,000. Walk away from your vehicle happiest in Ireland (34 per 100,000).

And in the US?

Overall, your risk is highest in the Northeast, lowest in the Midwest. You're most likely to lose your wheels in Washington, D.C., followed closely by Massachusetts and Michigan. You're about ten times less likely to have your car stolen in South Dakota than in Washington D.C.

Where is a European woman most likely to commit a murder?

French woman are the most dangerous in this category. There, 13.08 per cent of murders are committed by women. The Greeks are safest, at 6.7 per cent.

Am I more likely to be killed by a blunt object or by strangulation?

Blunt instrument murders account for 13 per cent. Strangling's more frequent at 15 per cent. But watch out for sharp objects (33 per cent). And worry least about what you're eating or drinking: poisoning takes lowest place at 2 per cent.

Am I more likely to be robbed in my home or out on the street?

You're six times more likely to be robbed on a street than in a residence, two times more likely to be robbed in a residence than in a corner shop, and nine times more likely to be robbed in a residence than in a bank.

Am I more likely to be killed by another human or by some other animal species?

According to one study you are 34 times more likely to be intentionally done in by a fellow human than by all the other species combined (excluding infectious organisms).

Is a man or a woman at highest risk of serving a long prison sentence?

Men serve, on average, nearly nineteen months in prison. Women typically serve just under eighteen months.

What crimes classified as 'serious' by government authorities am I most likely to be arrested for?

Larceny/theft.

Which crime classified as 'non-serious' am I most likely to be arrested for?

Driving while intoxicated.

Are men or women more likely to be reported in child maltreatment cases?

More than 60 per cent of those reported for maltreatment of children are women.

6

DOCTOR, WHAT ARE MY CHANCES?

◆

It's never been a better time to be a baby (or to have one). Mortality rates for babies have tumbled, more than halving in the UK in only twenty-odd years. Medical knowledge is advancing all the time, and diseases and infections that used to be incurable now carry very little risk. Sadly, this knowledge has not spread equally throughout the world, and a commonplace illness like measles remains a major killer.

The sudden appearance of new illnesses is frightening. AIDS has caused particular alarm, but it has not, as yet, reached the terrifying levels predicted. It is still a relatively rare way to die and the precautions you can take against it have been well publicised. It is far easier to catch syphilis, and there are numerous illnesses, ranging from flu to lung cancer, which are more common causes of death.

In the West we are becoming victims of our prosperity. The illnesses which have become the main causes of premature death – heart disease and cancer – are those in which over-consumption of various kinds plays a major part. Smoking at all and drinking too much are obvious culprits here, as is eating too much of the wrong foods and taking no exercise. All these increase the risks of early death, and all can be avoided (even if it's difficult sometimes, as later chapters will show).

But let's not be too gloomy. Life expectancy keeps increasing, and there's a very good chance you will die peacefully of natural old age.

How safe is circumcision?

Pretty safe. But 200 people lose their lives as well as their foreskins from undergoing this procedure each year in the USA alone. Thousands more require emergency medical intervention and 'corrective' surgery.

If I'm a male infant, where am I most likely to retain my foreskin – Britain, Australia, Canada, or the US?

Britain – where 98 per cent of all male infants now get through childhood 'uncut'. (The circumcision rate in Britain used to be very high. It seems that the medical 'need' for it evaporated when the National Health Service decided to stop paying for the surgery.) 78 per cent of all male infants retain their foreskins in Australia, 76 per cent in Canada and only 60 per cent in the US. Some doctors, incidentally, now perform foreskin reconstruction.

As I grow older, am I more or less likely to catch colds?

Less likely. After the age of 65, you have only a 14 per cent chance of catching a cold in any given year, compared to a 20 to 76 per cent chance for younger age groups.

Are males or females more likely to catch colds?

Boys more than girls, women more then men.

How risky are medical X-rays?

Most authorities consider them, for the most part, safe. But you should be aware that a US survey indicates that more than 45,000 fatal cancers may be induced by medical X-rays each year.

Are some X-rays riskier than others?

Yes. All medical X-rays pose some danger, but the amount of radiation you are exposed to in some radiological studies of the gastrointestinal tract, for example, is 90 times what you are exposed to during a typical dental X-ray.

If I'm having surgery, at what time of the year are complications most likely to follow?

It's been a joke in medical circles for some time that July is a bad time to have surgery because that's when the teaching hospitals typically bring in new interns and residents. It turns out this may not be a joke. A study at the Veteran's Administration Medical Center in Denver, Colorado recently found that complication rates for medical treatment, and for surgical procedures in particular, escalate from 20 per cent in June to 50 per cent in July. Perhaps you'll want to opt for a tan, rather than surgery, in July; it may be safer.

What is the chance that what I'm going to see the doctor about will turn out to be of little consequence?

Among the complaints presented to primary-care physicians, 30 to 60 per cent, according to various surveys, have little, if any, health significance.

If my child is short at the age of 3, does that mean he/she is at risk of being short as an adult?

There is a good correlation between the height at the age of 3 and height in adulthood. You can calculate how tall your child will be in adulthood by measuring the child at the age of 3 and multiplying by 1.87 for boys and 1.73 for girls.

If I sleep with my pet, is it risker for me or the animal, from the point of view of passing on disease?

The risks are about equal – very low for both human and pet (provided we're talking about cats and dogs). Tuberculosis and ringworm are among the diseases that, in rare cases, can be traded.

Are males or females more likely to be hospitalised?

Even though men are injured more often than women, females are 15 per cent more likely to be admitted to hospitals – even when admissions for childbirth are excluded.

What are the risks of smoking during pregnancy?

Among women who smoke regularly, there is up to a 35 per cent higher risk of death to the unborn baby in the eight weeks before birth – and the same increased risk to the baby in the first week after birth. Smoking is not recommended at any time during pregnancy – but risks are especially high when smoking continues after the fourth month of pregnancy and when more than ten cigarettes are smoked per day.

If I'm pregnant, is there any risk in my working with a computer terminal?

Perhaps, according to a recent study conducted by researchers at the Kaiser-Permanente Medical Care Program in Oakland, California. Women who use terminals for more than 20 hours each week during the first three months of their pregnancies are nearly twice as likely to have miscarriages. However, whether the terminals themselves or job-related stress (or both) are responsible remains to be determined.

Are boys or girls at greater risk of dying before birth?

Boys have a 25 to 30 per cent greater risk of dying in the womb.

What are the chances I will die while giving birth?

Nil, if you're from Luxembourg. Very low (0.02 per 1,000) if you're Norwegian. Middling, in the UK (0.07) and highest in France (0.14).

What is the risk that my baby will have to be delivered by Caesarean section?

21.1 per cent overall. The chance increases with age to more than 35 per cent for expectant mothers aged 35 and over.

What are the chances my baby will die in its first year?

The average European infant mortality rate is 10 in 1,000. Figures in the UK have improved from 18.8 per 1,000 (1967) to 9.1 last year. Infant mortality is highest in Portugal (16.7) and lowest in Denmark (7.7).

Which is more risky, legal abortion or pregnancy/childbirth?

You are 10 times more likely to die during pregnancy/childbirth than during a legal abortion (8 in a million, versus 80 in a million).

Are legal abortions appreciably more risky later in pregnancy, compared with early in pregnancy?

Yes. The risk of the mother dying increases twenty-four-fold if she has the abortion after the thirteenth week of pregnancy (as compared with having it in the first nine weeks of pregnancy).

What are the chances my hysterectomy wasn't necessary?

Up to 30 per cent of all hysterectomies are unnecessary, according to some experts.

Is a woman more likely to have a hysterectomy in the US, England, France, or West Germany?

The US woman is 2 to 3 times more likely to have a hysterectomy.

What are the chances my pregnancy will result in twins – or more?

Slightly over 2 per cent.

Where are my chances of multiple birth highest?

Fertility rates are highest in Ireland, with an average of 2.3 children per woman. It's lowest in Italy (1.3).

Do my chances of having a multiple-birth pregnancy increase or decrease with age?

Increase. The multiple-birth rate for women aged 35 to 39 is nearly triple that of females under 15 (6 per 1,000 live births versus 15.8 per 1,000 live births among the older women).

What are my chances of giving birth to a baby with congenital abnormality?

Figures are hard to come by. In England and Wales, Down's syndrome occurs in 6.7 of every 1,000 births, spina bifida in 3.1 and cleft palate 3.7.

What is the risk that a married woman (15 to 44) will be infertile?

Excluding the surgically sterilised, the risk is about 14 per cent.

Due to infertility problems I want to have a baby via an embryo transfer procedure. What are the chances of success?

17 per cent that you will become pregnant by this method, 11 per cent that you will deliver a live baby.

Is there any risk in wearing tight-fitting Y-fronts?

An increased incidence of infertility has been reported among men who habitually wear tight-fitting trousers and/or underpants. This reduction in fertility is reversible upon going back to looser-fitting clothing.

Is there any truth to the rumour that anaesthetists and jet pilots are more likely to give birth to girls?

Yes, various studies over the years have confirmed that men who are exposed to a lot of toxic chemicals, high heat, unusual pressures (jet pilots, deep-sea divers) are more likely to father girls than boys. Apparently these stresses kill off the slighter smaller and presumably less hardy, male-producing sperm more easily than they do the larger, hardier female-producing sterm.

Are men or women more likely to contract fatal illnesses?

Men.

Are men or women more likely to have non-fatal illnesses?

Women are much more likely to have these illnesses.

What are the chances I will experience a dozen or more symptoms of ill health in any given year?

Excellent. Top of the list will be headache, tiredness and backache. Back pain is the most frequently undiagnosed ailment. Only 10 per cent of sufferers will consult their doctor.

Overall, are the risks of dying from cancer increasing or decreasing?

Since 1985 lung cancer deaths in men have begun slowly to decline. However, rates among women are still rising rapidly with mortality rates three times those of 35 years ago. Lung cancer will soon overtake breast cancer as the chief cause of death by cancer in women in developed countries.

What are the chances I will survive at least five years if I have just been diagnosed as having cancer?

Your chances are as follows, depending upon the type of cancer: pancreas, 3 per cent; oesophagus, 5 per cent; lung, 13 per cent;

stomach, 17 per cent; leukaemia, 33 per cent; ovary, 38 per cent; kidney and rectum both, 50 per cent; colon, 53 per cent; cervix, 66 per cent, prostate, 70 per cent; breast, 74 per cent; bladder, 75 per cent; skin, 80 per cent; oral cavity, 83 per cent.

Am I more likely to die of diabetes or cancer?

You are about 14 times more likely to die of cancer.

Am I at greater risk of dying in an accident or from heart disease?

You are approximately 30 times more likely to die from heart disease than from a road accident, and 15 times more likely than from any type of accident.

Am I more likely to risk an unproven medical treatment if I have arthritis or cancer?

38 per cent of all arthritis suffers have tried unproven remedies, while only 15 per cent of all cancer patients have resorted to these.

Has the risk of dying from breast cancer gone down since routine breast X-rays to detect early cancers were recommended?

No. The death rate has remained nearly unchanged for almost twenty-five years. Health officials say the reason for this is that most women are not having regular breast X-rays. A recent survey indicates that 62 per cent of all women of 40 or older have never had a breast X-ray; 17 per cent said they didn't even know such cancer-detecting breast X-rays (called mammograms) exist. Health officials have been recommending for some time that women aged 40 to 50 have these X-rays at least once every two years and annually after age 50. They believe breast cancer mortality can be reduced by 30 per cent if women follow these recommendations. There are currently about 135,000 new breast cancer cases and 42,000 breast cancer deaths annually.

What are the chances a precancerous cell change will go undetected after a single cervical smear?

1 in 3, according to some authorities.

Do more people die on the roads or from adverse reactions to a prescribed drug each year?

On the roads. Adverse reaction deaths number about 0.1 per 1,000. Road deaths go from 14 per 1,000 in the UK to 42 per 1,000 in Ireland.

Are men or women more likely to have haemorrhoids?

Men are 5 per cent more likely to suffer.

Are men or women at greater risk of being constipated?

Women, 2.53 times as often as men.

Are men or women more likely to have bunions?

Women suffer from this affliction 3.35 times as often as men do.

Do men or women suffer more often from high blood pressure?

Women, contrary to popular belief. Men, however, die more often from damage caused by this disease.

Migraine headaches have been characterised as the curse of the rich and/or the smart. Does the incidence of migraine increase with socioeconomic status?

No, in fact the opposite is true. The risk of migraine goes down as you move up the socioeconomic scale.

What are the chances my cholesterol level is too high?

According to figures some think are too conservative, 25 per cent of all Americans have cholesterol levels so high they are at serious risk of coronary heart disease. In the UK those who are concerned about cholesterol intake recommend daily intake of 300mg. The average Briton takes between 350mg and 400mg.

Does lowering cholesterol really reduce the risk of heart disease? By how much?

Yes, it does – and dramatically. For every 1 per cent reduction in your blood cholesterol you earn a 2 per cent reduction in the risk of coronary heart disease, according to an advisory panel of the US National Institutes of Health.

I've heard that body shape can be a risk factor for some serious diseases? Is that true?

Yes, men are at increased risk of heart disease, diabetes, and stroke when their waists are the same size (around) or even bigger than their hips. Women are also at significantly increased risk when their hips are not at least 20 per cent larger than their waists. Upper-body fatness in men has been associated with a sixteen-fold increase in diabetes risk.

How likely am I to develop high blood pressure?

Pretty likely. More than 40 per cent of us have reached the boiling point. Blacks more often than whites have this affliction. (But see the next question.)

What are the chances my 'high blood pressure' has been misdiagnosed?

According to a US study at Cornell University Medical Center, as many as 21 per cent of those currently on lifelong medication for high blood pressure (hypertension) don't have this condition at all. Instead, they are suffering from harmless 'white-coat hypertension', which means their blood pressure is elevated only when the doctor measures it. Younger women are believed to be at the highest risk of this misdiagnosis.

Who is at greatest risk of dying of heart disease?

The Irish (89.25 per 100,000), then the Finns (82.73). Bottom of the list are the French (21.35). These rates are more or less the same for general diseases of the circulatory system, although the Portuguese have a high incidence of cerebro-vascular diseases (31.24).

What is the least amount I can exercise and still significantly diminish the risk of cardiovascular disease?

As little as twelve minutes three times a week – provided the exercise is of the aerobic variety.

When is jogging more hazardous than helpful?

Jogging in major urban areas, where air is polluted, is often more harmful to health than no exercise at all.

I'm thinking of buying an exercise bicycle. Will it be a waste of time and money?

Probably – but only because you're not likely to use it regularly. Only about 17 per cent of those who purchase exercise equipment actually use it more than once a week.

What are the chances I will stick to my new exercise programme?

Don't junk your armchair just yet. A number of studies indicate that 50 per cent drop out before they are six months into sweat. Fully 25 per cent don't even start their first session!

Where am I most likely to live longest?

If you're a man, head for Denmark. There, men over 65 form 6.2 per cent of the total population, whereas in Ireland they're only 4.7 per cent. Women live longest in West Germany, where the over-65s are 9.6 per cent of the total. Again, Ireland comes lowest with 5.9 per cent.

Where are women at least/greatest risk of dying of breast/cervical cancer?

For breast cancer the greatest risk is in the UK, with a death rate of 52.4 per 100,000. The rate is lowest in Spain (21.7). For cervical cancer, rates are highest in Denmark (5.95) and lowest in Luxembourg (1.81).

Am I more likely to die next year if I live in an inner city area, the suburbs, or out in the country?

Your chances of dying are greatest in the inner city. The suburbs, however, prove more conducive to life than the country.

In which developed countries do males have the longest/shortest life expectancies?

Longest in Japan (74.2 years) and Sweden (73.1), shortest in Singapore (68.7), Ireland (68.8), and Scotland (69).

In which developed countries do females have the longest/shortest life expectancies?

Longest in Japan (79.7) and Norway (79.4), shortest in Czechoslovakia (74.3) and Cuba (74.9).

How much better is it being a woman than a man when it comes to life expectancy?

Much. European women on average last between 5 and 8 years longer than men.

How much greater is the risk of dying of heart disease for a man than for a woman?

About double.

Which disease is most likely to kill me?

Ischaemic heart disease. It accounts for 20 per cent of all deaths in developed countries.

If I have a heart attack, how likely is it that it will kill me?

About 60 per cent of those who have heart attacks die instantly or within one hour of the attack.

How much of a risk is radon?

This odourless radioactive gas, a product of nature that wafts into dwellings from underground rocks, is currently blamed for about 13,000 lung cancer deaths in the USA yearly. 51 per cent of radiation exposure in the UK is from radon. Smokers exposed to the gas are at a risk of developing lung cancer 10 times greater than radon-exposed nonsmokers.

I'm thinking of having my diseased knee joint replaced with an artificial one. What are the chances the operation will succeed?

Very good: 9 out of 10 artificial knee joints are still functioning properly 11 years after the operation.

What are my chances of coming down with polio?

Virtually zero today – compared with 22 per cent in 1950.

How polluted is my environment?

From sulphur dioxide, the UK tops the league, with 3.5 million tonnes going into the atmosphere last year. Denmark did the least of this dumping (0.3 million tonnes). From acid rain, again the UK leads with 67 per cent of conifers dying, compared with 20.2 per cent in the Netherlands. Strangely enough those most aware of environmental issues appear to be the Italians (85 per cent). France and Ireland care least (56 per cent).

Where am I most likely to enjoy the longest life expectancy?

The Netherlands. Dutch men average 72.9 years, Dutch women 79.7.

In which city are my chances of surviving a heart attack best?

If it depends on there being a hospital bed available, then Luxembourg (12.5 beds per 1,000 population). Ireland fares ill with only 0.9. If what matters is the presence of a doctor, Italy leads with 42.4 doctors per 10,000 population and Ireland trails with 14.7.

How likely is it my friends will call me 'Four Eyes'?

Pretty good. About 56 per cent of the population wear spectacles, while only 3.6 per cent use contact lenses. More women (55.4 per cent) wear glasses than men (44.6) and many more women (63.1 per cent) wear contacts than men (36.9 per cent).

Will I keep my teeth?

With difficulty. Of the population of the UK aged over 16, no less than 26 per cent have 'no natural teeth'! (Nearly twice as many women as men.)

How likely is it that my hair will be white by the time I'm 50?

Averaging men and women together, there is a 50 per cent chance that half of your hair will be white by the time you reach the age of 50.

Does snoring pose any risk to health?

A study has appeared in the *British Medical Journal* that suggests snorers are at risk of more than just unhappy or angry spouses who can't sleep through the racket. Snorers, in this study, were found to be at twice the risk of non-smokers of heart disease and stroke! This remarkably increased risk held up even after the researchers took into account such other high-risk factors as smoking, alcohol consumption, obesity, and high blood pressure.

Who is more likely to be more physically active than average, the rich or the poor?

The well-off. Professional people are nearly three times as likely to walk over two miles a day as unskilled workers and are four times as likely to go swimming.

Is being poor a health risk?

Definitely. Death rates rise as income falls. This inequity is true at every stage of life. Babies of fathers with unskilled jobs are twice as likely to be stillborn or to die before the age of one as children of professional fathers. Unskilled workers are at twice the risk of death as professionals.

Which risk factors are the most important in terms of chronic disease and premature death?

Use of tobacco and alcohol, high blood pressure, 'over-nutrition' (obesity and high cholesterol), poor primary health care, especially during pregnancy, and situations that increase the risk of injury (certain jobs, sports, for example). Some 70 per cent of potential years of life lost are attributed to these six factors.

Are there are hidden risks in blood transfusions, apart from infectious agents?

A startling recent study at the Rochester Medical Center in New York State found that 43 per cent of colon cancer patients had recurrences of their cancers following blood transfusions, while only 9 per cent of those who did not have transfusions had recurrences.

If I am a man who never shaves, do I face any particular health peril?

Those who face you are more likely to feel imperiled. By not shaving for your entire lifetime you would save yourself 3,350 hours – but you'd have to be careful not to trip over your approximately 30-foot-long beard. You'd also have to worry about putting on an extra pound – in hair – every sixteen years. Yes, someone actually worked this all out, to the inch and the ounce. Not surprisingly, the study was funded by the Gillette Safety Razor Co.

What are the chances I'll be exposed to levels of noise sufficient to damage hearing?

About 5 per cent of people are exposed to levels of noise likely to cause hearing damage.

Am I more likely to die of AIDS or the flu?

The flu poses a far greater threat than AIDS to the general population. Influenza still kills about 70,000 people in America alone each year. The total of world deaths from AIDS so far is reported at 130,000, although there have probably been the same number of unreported deaths.

What is the risk of contracting AIDS from a blood transfusion?

Fewer than 2 per cent of AIDS cases are thought to be caused by blood transfusions.

Does AIDS or measles pose a greater risk to the world population?

Since AIDS emerged in 1981 it has probably killed fewer than 500,000 people worldwide; measles in that same period has killed more than 16 million.

Does AIDS or cigarette smoking pose a greater peril to society?

Smoking. The Centers for Disease Control state that diseases caused by cigarette smoking kill approximately 1,000 Americans every day. Cigarette smoking kills as many Americans in five weeks as AIDS has killed in ten years.

Which is more infectious – syphilis or the AIDS virus?

According to the Centers for Disease Control, syphilis is 400 to 500 times more infectious than the AIDS virus. The infection rate for the latter is less than 0.1 per cent male to female and less than 0.05 per cent female to male for heterosexuals not in a high-risk group (such as intravenous drug users).

Where in Europe am I most likely to catch AIDS?

Recent figures show that nearly 30 per cent of all new AIDS cases reported were in France. However, projections for future rates of increase were highest in Italy, Greece and Spain.

If I catch AIDS, what are my chances of survival?

If you register HIV positive, your chances of developing the disease increase with time, from 0.6 per cent after one year to 99.95 per cent after 20 years. The best guess is that up to 75 per cent of infected individuals will have full-blown AIDS within 6 years. Mean survival time is 13.75 months.

7

RISKY BUSINESS

Money, Education, Jobs,
Success, Failure

The arena of employment has become the major battleground of the sexes. And it looks as if women are gaining ground in the workplace (if not at home. . .). A high percentage of women with children now go out to work. There are more women in the professions – although the odds of becoming a professional are still not the same for men and women. And the pay gap between the sexes is narrowing overall.

But in the end, how much you earn depends, as it always has done, on the job you do. And that depends to a large extent on your education. Here boys are still doing better than girls, but not by much. Perhaps this difference has something to do with the extra attention they receive at school.

The highest earners are very likely to be graduates. High earners are also, not surprisingly, more likely to be happy with their work than the low-paid. But even among the higher-paid workers there are some interesting differences in earning power. It may come as a surprise to find that teachers earn more than civil servants and computer operators. Psychiatrists and psychologists don't seem to rate very highly compared with orthopaedic surgeons and biologists, but pilots are better off than chemists. In the US astrologists are in far greater demand than astronomers. What all this says for our sense of priorities is anybody's guess.

Lack of educational qualifications does reduce your likelihood of being well paid and increases your chances of being unemployed. But it does not necessarily prevent you becoming rich or achieving a place on the board. There are only a limited number of places at the top, but you can get there by hard work. And learning how to play golf will not go amiss.

In which country am I most likely to find a job?

Luxembourg, where only 2.2 per cent of the population are unemployed. Avoid Spain (19.6) and Ireland (17.8).

Will I be able to indulge in more of life's luxuries if I become a psychiatrist or an orthopaedic surgeon?

There's more money in bones than brains – a lot more. The typical orthopaedic surgeon makes twice as much as the average shrink.

How much more likely is a female today to be a professor, doctor, dentist, or judge than ten years ago?

Professor, 300 times more likely. Doctor, 30 per cent. Dentist, 60 per cent. Judge, less than 2 per cent.

Where will I earn most?

For manual workers, in terms of purchasing power, the best wages are to be had in Denmark. The average Briton earns only 88 per cent of the average Dane's wage. For non-manual workers in industry, the best place to work is Luxembourg. The lowest wages are to be found in Portugal (only 38 per cent of those in Luxembourg).

What are the chances that the main reason I will go to university is to make money?

71.3 per cent. Up from 49.9 per cent in 1971, when the majority of students cited presumably loftier reasons for seeking university degrees.

What are the chances I will seek a university education in order to develop a 'meaningful philosophy of life'?

Only 39 per cent. Down from 82.9 per cent in 1967. Four out of five graduates now head for the financial world.

If I'm a married man, am I still chief paymaster in the family?

No longer. 38 per cent of the time household bills are dealt with by the wife, only 32 per cent by husbands.

Will learning to play golf increase my chances of becoming a top executive?

It's not a sure thing, but be advised that 69 per cent of 200 top executives surveyed by the American magazine *Golf Digest* profess to be duffers who play more than twelve rounds of golf a year. So far as is known, however, Harvard has not yet made golf part of its MBA curriculum.

Looking back over the past five years, what were the riskiest/least risky investments?

Least risky were shares. Most risky were gold sovereigns, which actually went down in real value.

Looking back over the past fifteen years, what were the riskiest/least risky investments in the US?

US coins yielded the highest annual return over the past fifteen years – 18.8 per cent. By contrast, the annual return on diamonds over the past fifteen years comes to only 4.1 per cent. Shares managed a middling 9 per cent over the period.

What is the risk that my bank will go out of business and close its doors on me?

Very small. Currently about 8 out of every 1,000 commercial banks go out of business annually, worldwide. That's under 1 per cent.

What are the chances my newly-published novel will be one of the ten bestsellers of the year worldwide?

Forget fiction. The all-time most-translated international author is Lenin, with 2,354 versions to his credit. Even Shakespeare did only half as well. Agatha Christie managed a mere 920 translations and Dickens a miserable 604.

How likely am I to die without leaving a will?

Some 38 per cent of those aged 45 to 54 have not made a will at the time of their deaths; 27 per cent of those aged 65 and over don't leave wills. Interestingly, older people who are unmarried are less likely to die without a will than are married, middle-aged people.

Are men or women more likely to die without leaving a will?

Men. So much for the 'providers'.

What is the risk that my airline luggage will be lost, damaged, or delayed?

The last figures available show wide variability, depending upon the airline. Figures range from nearly 12 pieces of luggage per thousand lost damaged or delayed by TWA to under 4 pieces per thousand similarly mishandled by Pan American. British Airways lose less than 10. The industry average is 8. Recovery rate is 80 per cent within 24 hours.

I want to study medicine. What are my chances of getting into medical school?

It's crowded, but the easiest place to try is Italy. The least places in Europe seem to be available in Portugal.

Is it easier to get into Oxford or Cambridge?

Cambridge, where they accept 36 per cent. You stand a better chance in Arts than Sciences and the best chance of all in Classics (61.5 per cent acceptance).

Am I more likely to do well at school if I'm a boy or a girl?

Boys do marginally better than girls. Last year 63.46 per 1,000 boys passed national examinations, compared with 58.45 per 1,000 girls.

What science subject gives the best chance of good exam results?

Mathematics. Last year 35.69 boys and 26.85 girls per 1,000 passed national examinations in the subject. Hardest appears to be biology, where the pass rates were 11.73 and 9.35 respectively.

As a male, if I don't finish secondary school, am I really more likely to be unemployed?

Afraid so. While 6 per cent of all secondary-school-qualified men between 16 and 69 were out of work last year, those with no qualifications topped the 14 per cent level.

With all the publicity about the dangers of high cholesterol and fatty foods, I'm wondering just how risky it might be to go into the gourmet ice cream business?

Overall, not at all risky. The super-fatty gourmet types of ice cream are enjoying their greatest sales. Crisps, sweets and chocolates are also booming these days.

As a child under the age of one, I'm wondering what the risk is that Mum will be away working a lot of the time.

In two-parent households, with one or two children, in France there's a 58 per cent chance that the wife will work. In the UK the likelihood is 48.5 per cent and is lowest in Ireland (13.5 per cent). In the UK, however, 17 per cent of working women (married or not) with children of dependent age work full-time.

As a woman, what are my chances of becoming a high-ranking corporate executive?

5 per cent (compared with 9 per cent for men).

As a married woman with a job, what are my chances of getting help around the house from my partner in life?

A recent survey provides some depressing data. In only 6 per cent of cases does the man cook dinner. In only 22 per cent of homes does he do the dishes afterwards. In a mere 2 per cent of cases he does the ironing. Yes, most of the time he fixes the plugs (82 per cent). And while in only 2 per cent of households will he nurse sick children, 67 per cent of the time he'll share in their disciplining!

As a professional man, how likely is it that my working wife will also be a professional?

Most likely in the UK and France (46.8 and 42 per cent respectively) and least likely in Ireland (13.4).

What are the chances for my new business?

So-so. 50 per cent of all new businesses flop within five years. 70 per cent go out of business within ten years.

How risky are franchise businesses?

Far less risky than business in general. The worldwide failure rate for franchises is only about 2 per cent per year.

As a woman, how likely am I to earn as much as a man?

Overall, women earn 66 per cent of what men earn.

What are the chances I'll get a pension when I retire?

If you've paid full-rate contributions for more than 90 per cent of your working life, in most places you qualify for a State pension. 54 per cent of men and 33 per cent of women have occupational pensions.

Will working during my pregnancy put my baby at risk?

No, not under normal circumstances. In fact, not working seems to increase the risks. An American study at the University of North Carolina indicates that women who work during pregnancy are only half as likely as their non-working counterparts to have premature, low birth-weight babies.

What are the chances I'll still be working when I'm over 65 years of age?

It depends where you live. In the UK 7.5 per cent of men and 2.7 per cent of women over 65 are still working. In Portugal, however, the figures are 19.2 and 8.3 respectively. In Belgium the figures are 3.3 and 1 per cent.

If our health care continues to improve will we end up with a growing population of older people?

If present trends continue the number of pensioners in the population will rise from the present 30 per cent of the population to 73 per cent in 2025.

Is the world getting more crowded?

Less so in Europe than anywhere else. Forecast Eurogrowth is 2 per cent, compared with 17 in the USA, 9 in Japan, 19 in the USSR and 39 worldwide! Within Europe some countries are actually losing numbers. The population is expected to fall in Belgium (-4.4), West Germany (-4.3), Ireland (-3.6), Italy (-1.6) and Denmark (-1.0).

How serious is the risk that I will end up in a job I find unsatisfactory?

It depends upon how much the job pays. Only 29 per cent of those making more than £40,000 per year profess occupational dissatisfaction, while 48 per cent of those making under £10,000 per year are dissatisfied.

What risk will be uppermost in my mind on my wedding night?

Sexual or romantic risks? No. 67 per cent of all couples are most concerned about the financial risks of marriage – and, specifically, whether they will be able to afford one another the morning after!

Are there any hidden risks in having my spouse work?

You'll spend 37 per cent less time talking with one another than do couples with just one wage-earner; you'll also spend 40 per cent less time doing things together that you both consider fun.

Am I more likely to end up leaving £0 or £250,000?

Only 3.2 per cent of the adult working population is worth over £100,000. A few more make this exclusive club by the time they retire: 7 per cent. A whopping 58 per cent are worth less than £5,000.

Are housewives or career women more likely to have heart attacks?

Drop your apron and grab a briefcase. The risk of heart attack is almost twice as high for the housewife.

Are men who are employed or unemployed more likely to die of heart attacks?

Idle hands, bad heart. Being unemployed increases the risk of heart attack by 14 per cent among males 25 to 64.

Is being out of work likely to make me think of suicide?

In general the risk of suicide is 12 to 15 times greater among the unemployed. After that, it depends where you live. The highest incidence of suicide is in Denmark (28.19 per 1,000). The rate is lowest in Greece (3.84) and next lowest is the UK (8.53).

Are blue-collar or white-collar workers more likely to die next year?

Too much hard work apparently will kill you. Blue-collar workers are 41 per cent more likely than average to die next year.

Can I count on getting correct change at my local fast-food restaurant?

Not as often as you can count on getting the wrong change; according to a study at the American Hudson Institute less than half the 21 to 25-year-olds working in these establishments give the correct change for a two-item meal!

Is there much chance my car will be recalled because of some defect?

Yes. In fact, 60 per cent of all cars sold in the 1980s were recalled for one defect or another. Many of these were minor.

Is it really possible to get rich by hard work – or do you have to inherit it?

82 per cent of 'affluent' people (those who are worth £250,000 net or more, exclusive of their homes) say they got rich by working hard; only 6 per cent inherited wealth.

How much more likely am I to have an annual income in excess of £40,000 if I complete a university degree as opposed to finishing my education after secondary school?

Twice as much. That's how much more degree-holders earn on average more than non-degree-holders.

What chance have I got of reaching the top earning bracket?

Only 4.1 per cent of people make more than £30,000 a year.

What's the chance I'll be a top executive of a major company if I didn't go to university?

Not too great, but not out of the question. A recent US survey showed that 12 per cent of top executives never went to university.

Am I more likely to be a top business executive if I start out as a labourer or as a lawyer?

Labour seems to provide better experience for leadership than does the law. About 10 per cent of today's top executives climbed up from manual work beginnings. Only 6 per cent started out as lawyers.

Where are the best chances of a job teaching literacy skills?

Go south. The highest European illiteracy rate by far is Portugal, with 20.6 per cent. Or you could go East. India leads the world league table with 59.2 per cent illiteracy.

What are the chances I will complete four years of university?

Good, once you're in. Drop-out rates average only 10 per cent overall, although the rate is highest (50 per cent) in the first year. Medicine and education students seem to stick at it best and 'Professional Studies' worst.

Is an older or newer house going to be riskier in terms of energy costs?

On average, energy will cost you 35 per cent more if you buy or rent a house built before 1940.

Is a business more likely to fail than it was thirty years ago?

Yes. Twice as likely.

Is there any risk in wearing a tie?

Yes, and you don't have to hang yourself with one to be at risk. US researchers at Cornell University conducted a study showing that 66 per cent of all businessmen wear their ties too tight. 12 per cent wear them so tight they actually reduce blood flow to the brain, diminishing cerebral function. It would be interesting to see how much a company's official loose-tie policy would increase productivity and revenue, not to mention blood supply.

What are the chances I will have to commute for one or two hours to get to work?

Low. Only about 5 per cent of Europeans live further than 1 hour from work. 75 per cent live within 30 minutes of work. The exceptions are France and Germany where nearly 10 per cent commute up to two hours (this may say more about the state of their roads than anything else!).

Where will I earn the most money?

In purchasing power, you'll do best in Denmark and Luxembourg, earning three times what you would make in Portugal.

Am I more likely to find work as an astronomer than as an astrologer?

Yes, in the US. In that country it appears there is considerably more demand for those who divine, rather than detect, the stars. In the US there are 13,000 astrologers and only 3,000 astronomers.

Is it all likely that one could work full-time and still be at the poverty level of income?

Yes. In fact, nearly 30 per cent of families with a full-time working member receive income below the official poverty level.

Which sort of person is most likely to pay over the odds for a new car: the person who shops around a lot, the person who distrusts dealers, or the 'loyal type' who sticks with the same dealer car after car?

The person who distrusts dealers and hates the whole process of buying cars is, ironically, the one who, according to a California market research firm, will pay over the odds. In fact, this person is three times more likely than any other to pay more than the list price for a car. This person doesn't shop around, rushes into the buying process without any prior research, makes his decision in haste and moves on. The careful shopper – the person who may spend a month or longer looking – is the least likely to overpay. The loyal type falls in the middle ground.

In terms of income, is it riskier going into biology or psychology?

Psychology – the pay on average will be about 40 per cent less.

How expensive is it to get a degree?

It costs three times as much to train a medic as it does to get an undergraduate degree in the Arts. But medics are twice as costly as architecture, biology, engineering and physics students.

What are the chances I will finish secondary school if I give birth before I reach 18?

53 per cent of girls who leave school to have a baby do not return.

I know teachers are badly paid, but are they worse off than other public servants?

No. On average teachers get 10 per cent more than civil servants.

I'm suing the media for libel. What are my chances of winning?

Not good. A recent survey reveals that three out of four libel cases get thrown out of court without trial. When the remaining cases do go to trial, plaintiffs such as yourself lose 80 per cent of the time. Looking back over several years, moreover, it is clear that the trend is increasingly in favour of the media in these cases.

My daughter wants a formal wedding. What's the financial risk to me?

Between £2,000 and £3,000, if you're footing the entire bill. That's the average cost of a formal wedding, according to *Brides* magazine.

I'm trying to decide whether I can afford marriage. What's the honeymoon going to cost me?

Average honeymoon expenditure in one recent survey was £3,000.

What are the chances I will die before my 25-year mortgage is paid off?

If you are a 30-year-old male, your chances of this happening is 1 in 9; if you are a 45-year-old male, the risk increases to 1 in 3. For the 30-year-old female, there is a lesser risk of 1 in 16, increasing to 1 in 5 for the 45-year-old female.

What are my chances of living well on my pension?

It depends where. In the UK the State pension averages 24 per cent of a person's average gross earnings. In Belgium the figure is 60 per cent, France 50 per cent and the Netherlands 42 per cent.

What are the chances that when I'm retired I'll still have to pay income tax?

For those who work after retirement, 18 per cent of married couples pay tax, 10 per cent of single men and 6 per cent of women.

Is it becoming riskier/less risky to be a woman – in terms of pay?

Definitely less risky. The pay gap, which remained at about 40 per cent for decades, has now narrowed. For manual workers, women are 14 per cent behind in Denmark, 19 per cent behind in France, but lag behind by 22 per cent in the UK.

Which cars are least risky from the point of view of repairs?

Porsche is the most trouble-free, according to a recent survey of 75,000 car owners. Mercedes-Benz came in second, with Toyota and Nissan in a tie for third. The only American cars to make the top-ten list were Cadillac, Buick, and Oldsmobile.

Isn't it true that most people who work for minimum wages are teenagers?

Yes. 51 per cent of male teenagers earn under £75 per week. Similar wages are earned by only 10.7 per cent of the age group 18–20.

In school, do boys or girls get more attention from their teachers?

Boys – and this is true, according to a recent American study, from kindergarten through to university.

Will I make more money if I become a chemist or a jet pilot?

You'll fly financially higher in the jet. Pilots make, on average, over a third more than chemists.

Will I do better financially becoming a schoolteacher or a computer operator?

Surprisingly enough, you'll do better as a teacher, by more than 15 per cent.

Are blue-collar or white-collar workers the ones most likely to be financially hurt during a recession?

It depends on the currency. A cheap domestic currency boosts export-manufacturing orders and thus aids blue-collar workers.

How likely is it that I'll graduate with Honours?

Your chances are improving. 87 per cent of first degrees are honours and the number has steadily risen over the last ten years.

How likely am I to be late for work in the year 2010?

In Europe over the last 30 years average commuting speeds have remained the same. Any future hold-ups through increased car traffic are likely to be offset by the 10 per cent expected to telecommute (work on a terminal at home) by the year 2010.

Are the rich or the poor at greater risk of driving petrol-thirsty cars?

According to a recent American survey the poor get fewer miles per gallon than the rich. In fact, fuel efficiency (miles per gallon in automobiles owned) and average family incomes are directly correlated. Those with incomes less than £10,000 per year get 13.9 mpg; those who make between £15,000 and £25,000 get 14.6 mpg; and those with incomes above £30,000 get 16.1 mpg and better.

Is a video recorder (purchased for recording at home) a good investment risk, from the point of view of actually getting used much?

Yes, if you live in West Germany, where twice as many blank tapes are sold to VCR owners as anywhere else in Europe.

Are some home improvements, in terms of return on money, riskier than others?

Improvements that typically pay off include new paint, kitchen and bathroom refurbishing, fireplaces, skylights, ceiling fans, new light fixtures, new entrances and landscaping. Forget the swimming pool.

How are my chances of achieving political power if I'm a woman?

You won't do well in Greece or Spain (about 4 per cent of their representatives are female). Things are a bit better in the UK (6) and Portugal (8). Denmark, Sweden and France all have over 30 per cent.

If I'm homosexual what are the chances of being elected president of the United States?

At present, only 26 per cent of the electorate say they would consider voting for a homosexual running for the presidency.

What are the chances my son will become a doctor/lawyer/nurse?

For every 100,000 boys, 567 will become doctors, 1,170 will become lawyers, 150 will become nurses.

What are the chances my daughter will become a doctor/laywer/nurse?

For every 100,000 girls, 223 will become doctors, 682 will become lawyers, and 17,475 will become nurses.

What are the chances my son will grow up to be a professional football player?

Slim. In the UK about 0.01 per cent of the male population make the grade.

What are the chances my little Einstein will grow up to get a Ph.D.?

Eight out of every 1,000 will get a Ph.D. Now you know why professional football players make so much more than professors.

8

HIGH RISKS

Smoking, Drugs, Alcohol

The links between smoking and serious illness are now so
well documented that only the most foolhardy person can
ignore the risks. But that doesn't make it any easier to kick
the habit. There's nothing wrong with the occasional drink,
but too much will do you no good. Even marijuana, once
hailed by its supporters as a far safer drug than alcohol, is
not as benign as its users would like to think. It will also
increase your chances of getting a criminal record. And
abuse of drugs and alcohol are major contributors to crime
and accidents. Drinking and driving really is dangerous.

The risks of coming to grief through tobacco, drugs and
alcohol are high, but some people are at greater risk than
others. Here the odds are to some extent outside your con-

trol. The twin Aunt Sallys of inheritance and upbringing can be wheeled in to take part of the blame. The genetic links in the development of alcoholism are clearly established, and there are all sorts of factors in the way you are brought up which can affect your likelihood of smoking, taking drugs, or drinking too much. Divorce can also increase your chances of smoking and drinking heavily.

But whatever the causes, once you've started it can be difficult to stop. Habits which include an element of addiction can be hard to break. The success rates are not encouraging, but the odds against success are by no means impossible. So if at first you don't succeed, never mind. Just try again!

What are the chances I will be able to stop smoking with the help of hypnosis?

Figures provided by the US Smoking Cessation Research Institute indicate that your chances of quitting are actually better using willpower alone (about 1 in 4 compared to 1 in 5 using hypnosis).

Am I more or less likely to smoke as I get older?

The older you are, the less likely you are to smoke. Some 32 per cent of those aged 20 to 34 smoke, 31.5 per cent of those 35 to 44 smoke, 29.9 per cent of those 44 to 64 smoke, and only 13.5 of those 65 and older smoke.

Am I more likely to smoke if I am divorced?

The divorced are a breathtaking 56 per cent more likely to smoke than their married counterparts. Freud could no doubt make something of this.

Are men or women at greater risk of becoming smokers?

Smoking is apparently still the 'manly' thing to do. Males are 15.6 per cent more likely to smoke than females.

What are the chances I will be able to stop smoking without some sort of help?

About 25 per cent. Males, light smokers, and those facing serious illness are the most likely to be able to quit on their own.

Which is more dangerous, smoking an ordinary cigarette or a marijuana cigarette?

In terms of exposure to carbon monoxide (linked to coronary artery disease), smoking one marijuana cigarette is, typically, the equivalent of smoking five tobacco cigarettes. A UCLA School of

Medicine study has found that those who smoke just three or four joints a day suffer as much respiratory damage as those who smoke a whole pack of tobacco cigarettes a day. Water pipes, incidentally, have been found to be ineffective filters for either tar or carbon monoxide.

Does marijuana use increase the risk of any major mental illness?

In a fifteen-year study of more than 45,000 Swedish soldiers, researchers at the Karolinska Institute found that those who have used marijuana more than 50 times are 6 times more likely than non-users to develop schizophrenia. They found a consistent, direct correlation between the amount of marijuana use and the incidence of schizophrenia. Those who had used marijuana 11 to 50 times had a three-fold increase in their risk of developing schizophrenia. The Swedish researchers do not think that marijuana itself causes schizophrenia but that it may help to trigger it in those who are predisposed by other factors.

As a reader of Ladies' Home Journal, *how likely am I to have used marijuana or cocaine?*

According to the *Journal* itself, 28 per cent of its readers have used marijuana, 9 per cent have tried cocaine.

What is the probability that a young person, aged 12 to 17, has had marijuana or alcohol last month?

12 per cent for marijuana, 28 per cent for alcohol.

What is the risk my 12-year-old will experiment with marijuana?

14 per cent.

What are the chances my 17-year-old will get drunk this week?

Low. Although 60 per cent of 17-year-olds confess to having been 'a little drunk', it was only once in the last year.

Won't letting a child use drugs or alcohol early in life reduce the risk that he/she will go on to abuse those substances later in life?

No. The earlier a child begins using drugs/alcohol the more likely he/she will have health problems and increased dependence on the substance later in life.

Is my child more likely to recognise that alcohol or marijuana is a drug?

A recent US survey reveals that only 42 per cent of all fourth-graders know that alcohol is a drug, while 81 per cent recognise marijuana as a drug.

Are girls or boys more likely to experiment with a variety of drugs?

Girls.

What are the chances that when I commit a crime I will be high on drugs or alcohol?

About 50 per cent.

What are the chances I will grow up to be a heavy drinker/a teetotaller?

8 per cent of all adults are heavy drinkers, while 35 per cent abstain entirely.

What is Europe's number-one drug problem among youth — alcohol, cocaine, marijuana, or heroin?

Heroin.

Are married men or divorced men/bachelors at higher risk of being heavy drinkers?

It appears that marriage, contrary to what some would have us believe, really is a refuge from, and not an invitation to, taking to the bottle. Some 66 per cent of all married men are either abstainers or light drinkers; only 34 per cent are heavy drinkers. For the bachelors and divorced men, just the opposite is true: 66 per cent are heavy drinkers, 34 per cent abstainers/light drinkers.

If I'm an alcoholic, how likely is it that I will be able to get off drink and stay off it?

Fewer than 10 per cent of all alcoholics are able to abstain entirely from alcohol for as long as four years.

The ten-year-old son of my American friend appears to be drunk every now and again. Is this at all likely?

Yes. The US National Council of Alcoholism reports that 100,000 ten- and eleven-year-olds get drunk at least once a week.

My parents are alcoholic. Does this increase the risk of becoming an alcholic myself?

Yes. You have a four times greater risk of becoming alcoholic than do the children of non-alcoholics.

If I'm the son of an alcoholic but am adopted by non-drinkers, am I still more likely than average to become an alcoholic myself?

Yes. You are still four times more likely than average to become an alcoholic yourself.

Is a home in which parents abstain entirely from alcohol the least likely to produce adolescents who drink heavily?

No. There is mounting evidence that a totally negative attitude toward alcohol can do as much to encourage adolescent drinking as a totally permissive or uncaring attitude.

Is there any link between television and alcoholism?

No one knows for sure, but it has been calculated that the average child will see booze consumed on TV an average of 75,000 times before he/she reaches the legal drinking age.

Are women in their childbearing years more or less likely to use drugs and/or alcohol?

More likely. 72 per cent more likely to use marijuana, 14 per cent more likely to use heroin, 61 per cent more likely to use cocaine, 61 per cent more likely to use alcohol regularly – more likely in each instance than the general population.

What are the chances that if I'm involved in a serious swimming or boating accident I've been drinking heavily?

Pretty high: 30 to 50 per cent.

Would placing higher taxes on beer reduce the risk of road fatalities among young people?

The US National Council on Alcoholism states that increasing excise tax on beer, the most popular alcoholic drink among young people, would reduce consumption and could cut alcohol-related fatalities on the roads by as much as 45 to 50 per cent for 18- to 20-year-old men and women. Alcohol-related road deaths are the leading cause of death among 15- to 24-year-olds.

Is alcohol more dangerous for men or women?

Alcohol is more toxic to women than to men. Alcohol becomes more concentrated in the blood of women than in the blood of men because males have more body water to dilute the alcohol. Thus it takes far less alcohol to inflict serious liver and brain damage in women.

Am I more likely to be an alcoholic if I'm a Baptist or an Orthodox Jew?

Baptist. Orthodox Jews are almost never alcoholics.

Who is more likely to have to be hospitalised for alcohol/drug abuse, blacks or whites?

A recent US study shows that blacks are about 35 per cent more likely than whites to be hospitalised for alcoholism and about twice as likely to be hospitalised for drug abuse.

Am I more likely to be hospitalised for alcohol abuse or for drug abuse?

Overall, Americans are four times more likely to be hospitalised for alcohol abuse than for drug abuse.

What is the risk my too-young-to-drive teenager could be a passenger in a car next month driven by somebody on drugs or alcohol?

38 per cent.

Where am I at greatest risk of falling in with beer drinkers?

Head for Germany, with the highest consumption in Europe. However, if you prefer to visit Czechoslovakia, they're only second by a glass or two.

Where am I at greatest risk of being exposed to serious wine drinkers?

If by serious drinkers you mean those who take the matter seriously and copiously (not that it necessarily makes them plastered) then

Italy's the place, with an average annual consumption of 160 pints per head.

Where am I at greatest risk of rubbing shoulders with spirit drinkers?

Hungary tops the list at 8.4 pints of 100 per cent alcohol-equivalent per year per head.

Am I at greater risk of abusing tranquillisers if I'm a woman or a man?

If you're a woman – simply because women far more frequently use tranquillisers.

What is the chance that a child has ever tried drugs?

A recent UK survey showed that up to 8 per cent of 11- to 16-year-olds have tried 'hard' drugs.

Does cocaine use during pregnancy increase the chances of subsequent cot death?

Yes – by 50 times.

In which part of the UK is drug use most prevalent?

In terms of those involved with drug offences in any way, England has by far the most prevalent use, Northern Ireland the least.

9

FAT CHANCE

Food, Diet, Weight

Diet and exercise books are runaway bestsellers. Our appetite for them seems insatiable. Mostly written for women by women, they sell in their millions in these health-conscious times. This should be no surprise when you consider that more than half the female population thinks it is overweight. But weight problems are every bit as common for men, and there is some evidence that fat men's careers suffer as a result of their obesity. Not to mention their health. But a good number of men are apparently blithely unconcerned.

Women have a much greater chance of developing unhealthy food habits such as compulsive overeating. And women are far more concerned about their size and shape than men. Nobody knows whether women really diet to please themselves, other women or men, but it looks as if whittling your waist will not necessarily win you your man.

There are fashions in body shape which you can't hope to keep up with. The chances of a statuesque Marilyn Monroe lookalike transforming herself into a waiflike Twiggy are not good. And now food has become a fashion victim too. Ideas about which foods are good for you change with bewildering speed. A trip to the supermarket can be an exhausting affair as you pick and choose between the risks on offer. Will that chicken give you salmonella? Or those eggs? And what about the additives? For every new fashion there's a diet to match, each one promising a painless path to a slim and healthy new you. The feature they all have in common is that, over the long term, they simply don't work for most people.

Only one thing's certain. Too much food makes you fat. The person who can find the key to safe and permanent weight loss will go a long way to improving our health. And they will make a fortune. Which brings us back to those diet books. . .

In which country of the world are people at the highest risk of being obese?

In the United States.

Am I at greater risk of being fat if I'm a man or a woman?

According to a US poll, 66 per cent of the men were overweight, compared with 63 per cent of the women.

Are men or women more likely to acknowledge a weight problem?

Women are more likely than men to consider themselves over-weight, even though men are actually just as likely to have weight problems. 59 per cent of women surveyed think they weigh too much, while only 37 per cent of the men do.

Are the rich or poor more likely to be overweight?

The poor. The Duchess of Windsor once said you can never be too rich or too thin. There does seem to be a relationship between the two.

What is the risk that, as a teenager, I will be dissatisfied with my weight and will either be dieting or trying to build myself up?

Nearly 60 per cent.

If I stop smoking, is there really a risk that I'll gain weight?

Yes. People who stop smoking gain, on average, eight pounds. Females tend to put on more than males.

As a woman, by how much will I increase my desirability among men if I become decidedly thin?

Probably not at all. Even though a recent Gallup Poll shows that most women think men desire a truly thin woman, the same poll indicates that men actually want a more average body type in their mates. Only 18 per cent of the poll's male respondents said they desired a thin woman as opposed to one of average build. Average is 5' 3" and 8st. 6lb. (dress sizes 10–12).

Are males or females more likely to be bulimic (binge eaters who induce vomiting)?

Females – up to 5 per cent. Males – less than 1 per cent.

I'm a woman with a weight problem. If I cut out drinking, how much faster can I expect to lose weight?

Not at all faster. Researchers at the Centers for Disease Control, Atlanta and at Johns Hopkins University have reported that, compared with non-drinkers, women who consume alcohol 7 to 13 times per week consistently lose more weight – just the opposite of what everyone had thought. These conclusions are based on two massive national food-intake surveys, and the association between alcohol consumption and reduced body weight was found to be substantial.

Does being an overweight male MBA put me at any particular financial risk?

According to a study from the University of Pittsburgh, the overweight male MBA earns $4,000 a year less than his lean counterpart. We do not know yet what financial fate awaits the overweight female MBA.

Are women's magazine readers more likely to become addicted to dieting, compulsive overeating, or sex?

They are at highest risk, according to a recent *Ladies' Home Journal* survey, of being compulsive overeaters (20 per cent). Fewer are addicted to dieting (8 per cent) and fewer still to sex (4 per cent).

Does my risk of eating food from takeaway restaurants increase or decrease with age?

Your exposure to greasy hamburgers and their like decreases steadily with age. Those aged between 15 and 19 have a 16 per cent likelihood of calling into a fast-food outlet this week, whereas those aged between 33 and 44 have a 12 per cent chance and those aged 65 or over have only a 9 per cent chance.

By how much will the use of artificial sweeteners help me lose weight?

By zero. In fact, according to an American Cancer Society study of 79,000 women, those who use artificial sweeteners are actually more prone to weight gain than are non-users. This held true despite the initial weight or types of food.

I like to please my dinner guests. Which meats, in terms of the ordinary palate, are served most often?

Firstly, dinner invitations from you will be considered a definite culinary risk if you are in the habit of serving offal of any type. You'll do best with poultry, almost as well with beef and veal, less so with pork and not well at all with lamb or mutton. (But none of it's as socially risky as offal!)

Is it risky to stop drinking milk as we get older?

Those who don't drink milk are three times more likely to develop colorectal cancer than do those who drink a couple of glasses of milk daily.

I've heard that on the typical diet each of us eats a ton of fat in our lifetime. Is that possible?

The typical UK diet actually puts the average individual at risk of consuming, over a lifetime, nearly 6,000 pounds of pure fat.

What is the chance I will consume a dozen or more pounds of cheese in a single year?

If you are an average Briton, the chance is 100 per cent. The typical Briton currently eats 13.4 pounds of cheese per year, 65 to 75 per cent of which is fat.

I love chocolate, but I just nibble at it. Is there a chance I am eating too much?

Considering its high fat content and considering the fact that the average Briton now eats 20 pounds of chocolates per year, yes, there is some risk. Americans now spend £2,112 million on chocolates each year.

In terms of cholesterol, which food contributes most of this substance to the typical British diet?

Eggs contribute 34.3 per cent of all cholesterol consumed. Beef (steaks and roasts) comes in second, contributing 24.5 per cent. Milk provides 13.5 per cent. By contrast, fish provides only 2.8 per cent.

Which commonly-consumed takeaway food contains the most fat?

Fish & chips: 62 per cent. Fried chicken & chips: 54 per cent. Hamburger: 26 per cent. Bottom of the list, baked potato & cottage cheese: 6 per cent.

Is there any chance that if I ate sugar-coated cereals as a child I'll still be eating them as an adult?

Eating habits apparently die hard. The chances are 50 per cent.

10

ELEMENTS OF RISK

Weather, Pollution, Natural and Unnatural Disasters

The forces of nature are awesome. Earthquakes, hurricanes and volcanoes are capable of terrible devastation. The wind can turn houses into matchsticks and cars into tin cans. Vast tracts of land are at risk of becoming uninhabitable deserts as drought takes hold. Rain causes floods and landslides. We are powerless against these disasters. They make our ingenious technology look puny indeed. Yet still we tinker with nature, trying to defy it or tame it with intelligence, and upsetting its balance in the process.

The effects of our actions have only recently hit home. The discovery of the hole in the ozone layer and the problems created by man-made pollution are causing widespread anxiety. As yet, there is little agreement about what could or should be done to reduce the risks.

Sometimes the risks we take in daring the elements seem to defy logic. The probability of earthquakes along the San Andreas fault in California is extremely high. Yet the populations of the huge cities sited on the fault line have not moved somewhere safer. Instead they have adapted their building techniques to improve the chances of their houses and offices withstanding disaster and then, presumably, crossed their fingers. When the chances of devastation are so high, why do so many people choose to defy the odds? Perhaps it is just that risk-taking is not always rational. After all, we worry a lot about very unlikely events. Or perhaps the Californians are simply easy-going fatalists, enjoying the climate and the lifestyle while they can, and hoping for the best. It might never happen – who knows?

What are the chances that a devastating earthquake will hit Southern California again within the next twenty-five years?

50 per cent – and the experts say that such a quake, measuring 8.0 or more on the Richter scale, will kill 3,000 to 14,000 people, seriously injure up to 52,000 people, and will cause about $17 billion in property damage.

What are the chances that a huge earthquake will hit San Francisco Bay area again within the next twenty-five years?

50 per cent – at an estimated cost in lives of 3,000 to 11,000 and an estimated cost in property damage of $38 billion. Serious injuries could total 44,000.

I hate rain. Where is the risk of being constantly soaked lowest?

You might try Antarctica. There are spots where it has not rained for at least 100 years. In Europe, try Spain.

Is it more likely to be sunny on any given day in Paris or London?

Paris. 85 per cent of the days are sunny. In London the figure drops to 81 per cent. But why limit the choice? In Malaga 94 per cent of days are sunny. And Athens comes out best at 96.

Where is the risk of exposure to ozone air pollution the greatest?

Worldwide, the risks are greatest, in descending order, at Reykjavik, Oslo, Budapest, Lisbon, Potsdam, Cairo, Edmonton, Kagoshima and New Delhi.

How much of the world's surface is presently threatened with desertification – extreme aridity caused by falling water tables?

Perhaps as much as 35 per cent of the planet's surface faces this life-threatening peril. 850 million people presently live in these areas.

We used to hear a lot about the 'population explosion'. Has the risk of world overpopulation gone away?

Unfortunately not. It took hundreds of thousands of years for the human population to reach 1 billion in the year 1800. The next billion materialised in just 130 years (1930). The third billion took a mere 30 more years to produce (1960). Now, in less than two decades, world population has soared to more than 5 billion, and, by 2,000, there will be more than 7 billion humans alive on the planet. The world population is currently growing by more than 90 million people a year. A decade ago it was considerably less – 75 million. World population is actually growing even a little faster than some of the so-called 'alarmists' warned it would, twenty years ago. Food-production technologies, however, have not been able to keep up with the exploding population, with the result that more than half a billion people are now without even minimally-adequate nourishment.

In terms of health hazards, is it riskier to live in a modern, well-insulated building or in a draughty old one?

Riskier to live in the modern building, according to a number of studies. One of these compared 400,000 US army recruits, some of whom lived in a new modern barracks and some of whom lived in old barracks. The recruits housed in the new energy-efficient barracks had 50 per cent more respiratory infections than those living in the old buildings. The fresh air that gets into the old buildings apparently provides a healthier environment.

How likely is it that the new office building I'm working in has the 'sick building syndrome'?

According to the World Health Organisation, up to 30 per cent of all new and refurbished office buildings cause health problems.

11

HEADGAMES

Emotions, Stress, Self-Esteem, Mind, Spirit

Success was the buzzword of the 1980s and stress followed hard on its heels. High achievement can exact a high personal cost for its financial rewards. Materialism is on the way out. Gentler, less selfish philosophies are forecast as the successes of the future.

Materialism pays no heed to spiritual needs. The Churches may have lost their place at the centre of most people's lives, but there are many alternative outlets for faith. The extraordinarily high level of belief in UFOs may be flying in the face of reality. But attending to your emotional and spiritual wellbeing can have real benefits. Doing good to other people turns out to be a good bet for doing good to yourself, as does simply listening rather than talking. And you will help yourself by being sociable and trustful.

The odds against emotional health and happiness can sometimes seem unfairly stacked. Having parents with problems can be a problem later on, but it is something a child cannot avoid. And the high risk factors, such as bereavement, which make you more vulnerable to illness and suicide are simply part and parcel of the chances of life.

It is not unusual to need help when the going gets tough, but it is interesting that more women than men turn to a psychiatrist. Yet you are more likely to be admitted to a psychiatric hospital if you are a man. Perhaps this reflects traditional differences between the sexes. Women are less afraid to show their emotions and go for help at an early stage. Men try to hide their feelings and worries until the problems become more serious. Keeping a stiff upper lip is a well-known British characteristic, and not to be despised. But showing emotion can be a good thing too. It could even reduce your chances of developing cancer.

I attend church regularly. Am I in the majority?

Far from it. Average attendance at church in the UK has declined by 1 per cent per year over the last twenty years. Average congregation membership is 15 per cent of the population.

Will having a room of my own as a teenager increase or decrease my risk of mental illness later in life?

Decrease it.

What are the chances that I'll have a supernatural experience?

About 1 in 17, according to one survey. If you live in California your chances are more like 1 in 3 (according to Californians).

What are the chances I'll be a fingernail-biter?

The only known study of this fascinating subject was conducted by the US Army. Your chances of being a nail-chewer are 1 in 6 overall. More horrifying yet: fully 33 per cent of America's more than 40 million fingernail-biters are also toenail-biters! While 16.6 per cent of the general population regularly bites its nails, 25 per cent of all Army recruits and 40 per cent of all children/ teenagers do so. So there.

Do do-gooders have better immunity than Scrooges?

Yes, according to early studies at Harvard and elsewhere that suggest that altruism boosts immune response.

Will doing regular voluntary work diminish any significant health risks?

In an ambitious University of Michigan Survey Research Center study of 2,700 people, researchers found that, for men, doing voluntary work could increase life expectancy. There was a 2.25 times greater incidence of death among men (during the study period) who did no voluntary work, compared with men who volunteered at least once a week. Such dramatic differences were not noted for women – perhaps, the researchers surmised, because women are already involved in caring for others, typically their families.

Are poor listeners at higher risk of getting sick?

Yes, a recent study found that those who like to talk as much as possible and listen as little as possible are at increased risk of developing high blood pressure.

Do many people believe in astrology?

To the chagrin of the scientific community almost 40 per cent of people say they think astrology is either 'very scientific' or 'sort of scientific'.

Will people think I'm weird if I tell them I believe in witches and ghosts?

Maybe not crazy, but many will no doubt think you are a bit odd. Still, no less than 11 per cent of people share your belief in these supernatural entities, according to a Gallup poll.

Am I more likely to be truthful with a computer or a psychologist?

You're more likely to answer questions truthfully if they are put to you by a computer than by a psychologist.

Does brief separation of very young children from their parents pose any health risk to the children?

Some researchers believe that even day-care separation for children under six months old can pose risk, increasing susceptibility to various diseases later in life. Various studies show that separations, especially those caused by divorce, hospitalisation, or death of a parent, can result in immune abnormalities in children.

If I get into an argument with my parents, what are the chances I will win?

Not so good. Parents prevail almost 90 per cent of the time.

What are the chances that, as a university student, I will frequently or occasionally cheat in an exam?

30.4 per cent. Up from 20.6 per cent in 1966.

Does anxiety increase a woman's risk of having premenstrual tension (PMT)?

Yes. One survey revealed that 41 per cent of 'very anxious' women have PMT while only 21 per cent of 'calm' women do.

Does a full moon really increase the risk of 'madness' or other unusual behaviour?

An analysis of forty studies related to this issue indicates there is no correlation between moon phases and human behaviour. So, if your neighbour bays at the moon, he's perfectly healthy.

What are some of the major factors for mental and emotional problems faced by young children?

Researchers at George Washington University Medical School note that infants exposed to the following risks are more likely than others to have emotional problems and reduced mental ability, as measured by IQ: absent father, mother who suffers from mental illness at least twice in her lifetime, non-responsive mother who seldom smiles at or touches infant, highly anxious mother, head of household who is unemployed or unskilled, four or more older children in family. The researchers found that when none of these risks was present, the average IQ of the child was 118. IQ was found to decline steadily with the number of risks present. Other researchers confirm that factors such as these play crucial roles, especially in infants from birth to three years old. What happens during this period, these researchers believe, has a large impact on mental/emotional health and criminality in later life.

As a woman, what mental health problem is most likely to afflict me?

A phobia or irrational fear of something. Many phobias are characterised by panic attacks.

Does watching a lot of television pose any risk to my child?

Paediatric studies link childhood obesity with TV watching. Others worry that constant TV watching may diminish respect for human life. According to another study, between the ages of 5 and 15 the average child sees more than 13,400 people killed on television.

Is there a chance I'll never be satisfied with life?

Yes, but that risk declines steadily with age. Whereas most people fear growing older, satisfaction with life actually increases in direct relationship with age. According to a Harris poll, only 53 per cent of us profess to be satisfied with life when we are aged 18 to 24; that figure rises to 59 per cent among those aged 25 to 34, to 62 per cent among those aged 35 to 39, and to 72 per cent among those aged 50 and older.

Are people who mistrust others more likely to be untrustworthy themselves?

Yes. According to a number of studies, people who tend to be suspicious of others are themselves more likely to be cheats, liars or manipulators.

Are trustful people more likely to enjoy good mental/emotional health than the mistrustful?

Yes. A variety of studies show that trustful people, far from being the gullible, naive types who are victimised by others, are actually the kind of people others most frequently seek out as friends. They are far better liked and have far fewer mental/emotional problems.

Are trustful/mistrustful people likely to live longer?

Trustful individuals are significantly less prone to premature death than mistrustful people.

In terms of self-esteem and intelligence, is the 'only child' at a disadvantage compared with children who have siblings?

No. Studies indicate that only children usually have higher self-esteem than do children with siblings. Other studies indicate that they have higher IQs than do children who have many siblings.

Does a free display of emotion reduce health risks in men?

That's been the theory for some time. Now a US study at Johns Hopkins University School of Medicine seems to confirm it. This long-range study indicates that those who find it easy to show their feelings are 16 times less likely to get cancer than are loners who keep it all bottled up inside. This is true despite the fact that those who are openly emotional are the types most of us would think of as more unstable than the other types – they're subject to open bouts of anxiety, depression, 'acting out', and seem to be more easily upset. In reality, it seems that the other types, including those who express positive, upbeat attitudes, are merely concealing their anguish – to their detriment. The sunny, ever-optimistic types have a cancer rate in between the openly emotional and the closed-in loners.

Will I be regarded as a loony if I tell people I believe UFOs are real and not imaginary?

Several surveys have shown that more than half of people believe UFOs are real objects that could conceivably come from other worlds. Some 10 per cent of all Americans, for instance, say they have personally seen UFOs.

If I tell people I really believe in lucky numbers, will they look at me askance?

That's a risk you won't have to face at least 43 per cent of the time. That's the percentage of your fellow citizens who also firmly believe in lucky numbers. 12 per cent of the population also admits to a firm belief in lucky charms — which they carry with them whenever possible.

Does living with somebody reduce the risk of death?

It depends on whether you're male or female. Having company apparently agrees with males, but not with females. Women who live in a household with other people are 2 per cent more likely to die next year than are women who live alone. Males living with others have 14.3 per cent less chance of dying next year.

Does being a social person reduce health risks?

Apparently. A University of California, Berkeley, study of 5,000 people indicates that a rich social life significantly prolongs one's existence. Those with a network of friends, relatives, and links with community organizations were two times less likely to die during the study period than those who lived in isolation.

Is a petrol station attendant or a business executive at higher risk of heart attack due to psychological job stress?

The petrol station attendant. A study of nearly 5,000 men has shown that such supposedly low-responsibility, low-stress jobs as cashier, cook, petrol station attendant, and production-line worker are actually much more stressful than far higher-paying jobs which require advance training. The critical difference has to do with control. Those who have little control over their work were found to be two to four times more likely to have heart attacks than were those who have a lot of responsibilities (such as professionals and executives) but who have a great deal of control over their own work.

I feel that scientists are actually dangerous. Am I alone?

You're in company. 53 per cent believe scientists are dangerous people.

What are the chances I will win a decoration if I serve in the military forces during a major war?

The chances of war making you a recognised hero have varied little from World War I through to the Vietnam War. They are, overall, 2.6 in 10 million (remarkably similar to your chances of being killed by a poisonous snake).

If I take a polygraph test and lie, what is the risk I will be detected?

According to some studies, there's about a 72 per cent chance you will be caught by the machine.

What is the risk that if I take a polygraph test it will incorrectly say that I lied?

At least 1 in 15 will thus be falsely accused.

What factors will put me at risk of being perceived as boring?

The characteristics of the boring person, according to researchers at North Carolina University in America, are a penchant for complaining about themselves, frequently asking pointless, dead-end questions, showing little interest in others, and indulging in small talk.

How likely am I to change my plans because of an astrological forecast?

7 per cent.

Where am I most likely to visit a psychiatrist?

In terms of how available one is, Iceland, where the psychiatrist/population ratio is more than three times that of the UK. They're thinnest on the ground in Malta.

Is a 30-year-old or a 50-year-old more likely to consult a psychiatrist?

Those aged 25 to 44 are 50 per cent more likely to consult psychiatrists than those aged 45 to 64.

Are males or females more likely to consult psychiatrists?

Females are 37 per cent more likely.

Are male or female adults more likely to be admitted to a hospital for psychiatric care?

UK admission rates are: males, 341 per 100,000; females 461 per 100,000.

Are male or female children at greater risk of requiring psychiatric hospitalisation?

The risk is 9 per cent higher for the male child.

What is the risk I will be admitted to a hospital for psychiatric care next year?

2 per cent of the population are admitted each year.

If I am hospitalised for psychiatric care, is it more likely I will go voluntarily or be committed?

Contrary to the impression many soap operas still give, most (71 per cent) go voluntarily.

Does simply being in the military forces increase the risk of being admitted to a hospital for psychiatric care?

Yes. It almost doubles that risk.

Who is at the greatest risk of committing suicide?

Men in their 20s and 30s whose wives die.

Are the married or the unmarried more likely to kill themselves?

People who never marry are as unlikely to commit suicide as are the happily married. The divorced and those whose spouses die are at higher risk.

Am I really more likely to kill myself on or near a major holiday?

Recent studies suggest that the link between holidays and suicide is a myth – with one exception: New Year's Day. Apparently many people think New Year's Day is the appropriate time to act on their final resolution. Overall, however, holidays are actually a period of considerably fewer suicides.

Which Europeans are most likely to kill themselves?

Danes have the highest suicide rate in the EC.

In terms of contributing to the development of stress-induced major illness, which of the following 'life events' are the riskiest: divorce or marriage? Marriage or the death of a close family member? Pregnancy or foreclosure on a mortgage? Major personal injury or detention in jail? Christmas or a

fine for disturbing the peace? Making a major change in your eating habits or in your social activities?

Divorce is substantially riskier than marriage; marriage is a bit riskier than death of a close family member; pregnancy is quite a bit riskier than a mortgage foreclosure; detention in jail is moderately more risky than a major personal injury; Christmas is slightly more perilous than getting a fine for disturbing the peace; making a major change in your social activities is a little more dangerous than changing your eating habits.

What stressful life event most predisposes a person to a major illness?

Death of a spouse — followed, at some distance, by divorce and, in third place, marital separation.

12

SPORTING CHANCE

Sports and Gambling

For a professional sportsman the stakes are high. When the roll of the genetic dice throws up a high level of sporting prowess, the person with determination can earn a fortune. But the chances of becoming a top athlete are not good. And the risks of injury and burn-out are not too healthy either. Playing for fun is the best bet for most of us.

Professional gamblers play to win but this is not a game for the foolish or faint-hearted. Betting and gambling must be the last refuges of the optimist. The odds of winning in the long term are not good. But at least the risks are clear. The decision to place a bet is made in full knowledge of the odds. The amount bet is your choice. The potential losses and rewards can be calculated beforehand. But it takes a very cool head to beat the bookmaker. And only the most poker-faced punter playing strictly to the odds can come near to beating the table at cards.

For some people gambling becomes an addiction in which their heart rules their head at the expense of their pocket. For most of us it is confined to a flutter on the Derby or the National. There's always that sneaking hope that you might strike lucky. But there's no doubt that the best bet is to be behind the counter taking the money. It's the bookmaker who sets the odds, and it's odds on that he's the one who will drive away in the Rolls-Royce.

How risky is professional grand prix race-car driving?

One recent study indicates that the possibility of accidental death for the racer is at least 16.8 times greater than for the average white male.

Is it riskier being an active thoroughbred racehorse or a retired one?

Retirement may prove more hazardous to horse health. Some former racers become pampered pets, but more, the experts say, are turned into pet food.

What are the chances a secondary school athelete will compete in university as well?

50 per cent.

What are the chances that if I become a First Division football player I'll earn more than £125,000 a year?

Start looking for a tax haven. But if you're only going to make the Fourth Division, be sure it's love of the game that drives you on. Players there average £17,000 a year.

As a university athelete, what are the chances I'll get drafted by the professionals?

Only 8 per cent of young football players get invited to test. And only 2 per cent of those actually end up as professionals.

What are the chances my career as a professional football player will be a long one?

Not good. The average playing life is 8 years and most players are out of the game by their twenty-ninth birthday.

What are the chances that as a professional football player I'll have a disabling injury?

In the last four years, of 2,500 professional players last year, about 90 claimed injury retirement benefit.

What part of the professional football player's anatomy is at greatest risk of injury?

58 per cent of all major injuries in professional football involve the knee.

Does playing offensive or defensive games pose a greater risk of injury in professional football?

The risks are about equal.

Is it more dangerous playing football on artificial turf or the real stuff?

It's slightly more risky on the artificial stuff.

Am I at greater risk of spending money on lottery tickets if I earn a lot of money or little money?

The more money you make the less likely you are to buy lottery tickets. And by the way, the average return on your money from UK lotteries of all kinds is 29.86 per cent.

How risky is it to organise a lottery?

The most recent data show that of $21.7 million taken in ticket sales, $7 million was returned in prizes. Could be a good business to get into!

Am I more likely to gamble if I'm a Catholic or an atheist?

About 80 per cent of all Catholics confess to gambling now and then, compared with only 40 per cent of the atheists.

Are favourites in horse races really good risks?

Compared with all the other horses, yes. They win approximately 36 per cent of the time. Second favourites come in first 22 per cent of the time. Overall, punters overbet on outsiders (that is, they invest more money in outsiders than is justified by the rate of success) and underbet on the favourites — which is how horse racing stays in business.

As a regular racecourse punter, will I actually make money in the long run?

Fewer than 1 in 100 regulars actually make money at the races.

How much more likely am I to have the winning horse if my jockey is a professional rather than an amateur?

Not at all more likely. Your chances, either way, are approximately equal.

What are the chances I'll actually make money, long-term, as a gambler?

Terrible. About 1 in 5,000 gamblers regularly rake in a profit.

What is the chance that a professional poker player will resort to cheating?

Avoid Las Vegas next time you're feeling flush. According to some 'insiders' no less than 60 per cent of professional card-players in that home of gambling do it.

In poker, how much more likely is it that I will get a straight than a flush on the deal?

Your chances of being dealt a straight are about twice as good as your chances of getting a flush. You'll get a straight in 1 of every 255 hands dealt you, a flush in 1 of every 509 hands.

How often can I expect to be dealt a full house, four of a kind, a straight flush, or a royal flush in poker?

Don't stay up all night waiting. Your chances of getting the full house, on the deal, are 1 in 693, 1 in 4,164 for four of a kind, 1 in 72,192 for the straight flush, and 1 regal hand out of every 649,739 for the royal flush.

What are my chances for a pair or a triplet?

Get set for a pair, on the deal, every 2.4 hands, two pairs every 21 hands, three of a kind every 47 hands.

What are the chances I'll get a royal flush in two consecutive hands of poker?

Somewhat better than your chances of being killed in a plane crash.

In a full poker game, how likely is it that a professional will play up to and beyond the first bet?

Only about 25 per cent. Professionals spend most of their time not playing.

Overall, how much am I likely to win or lose, long-term, playing craps?

Overall you'll lose 16.7 per cent of what you gamble. If you stick to playing the odds, however, you'll break even over the long haul (averaging all players).

How much of a risk is roulette compared with craps?

Overall, people lose more of what they gamble at craps than they do at roulette. Whereas they'll lose more than 16 per cent of what they bet at craps, on average, they'll lose about 5 to 8 per cent, again on average, of what they bet at the roulette table.

ENVOI

◆

Do you still dream of winning the pools? Well, why not. We all
dream impossible dreams, and this is a dream that does come true
for the lucky few. But don't depend on it!

And that's the key. Once you know the odds, you can decide for
yourself how much you want to stake. Some people enjoy taking
risks; other people don't. Some people are naturally optimistic;
others are not. We're all different — thank goodness.

It would be silly to spend every waking moment calculating
risks. There is a story about the centipede who spent so much time
worrying about which leg to move next that he stayed glued to the
spot. No doubt in the end he was run over by a bus.

It would be equally foolish to ignore danger altogether. It is
dangerous to cross the road, but we all do it all the time. You can

only make sure that you look right, left and right again before you step off the pavement.

Of course, one of the greatest chances you take is one over which you have no control at all – the accident of birth. When, where and to which parents you are born all affect your life. Perhaps to a greater extent than almost any chance you take later, however careless or calculated that chance may be.

As human beings we have the unique capacity to reflect on our actions. We are not governed entirely by instinct. We can make decisions and choices, and those choices can themselves affect our chances of success. Francis Bacon once remarked that a man must make his opportunities as often as find them. There are no guarantees in life, whether of safety or success, health or wealth, good luck or bad. Life's a gamble. You can only weigh up the odds and take your chances. . .